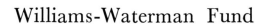

Williams-Waterman Fund

The author with Robert E. Waterman in 1937.

Williams-Waterman Fund

FOR THE COMBAT OF

DIETARY DISEASES

A History of the Period
1935 through 1955

by Robert R. Williams

49915

ST. JOSEPH'S UNIVERSITY   STX
RC620.A1W72
Williams–Waterman Fund for the combat of

3 9353 00009 5834

RESEARCH CORPORATION
405 Lexington Avenue · New York 17, N. Y.

RC 620, A1
W72

Contents

Copyright 1956, Research Corporation

PRINTED IN U.S.A.

CHAPTER I

Introduction

As Chairman of the Williams-Waterman Fund, I am writing this history upon retiring from that position after 16 years of the Fund's active operation. I regard this story in some sense as an accounting of personal stewardship. But I wish to emphasize strongly at the outset my feelings of gratitude and obligation to many other people who either took formative parts in setting up the Fund, or who guided its outlays and activities during two decades.

Indeed, the initial research which provided a basis for the Fund extends back more than 45 years. There were scores of persons who rendered some service during this long period. Some were my inspirational leaders, especially in the earlier years; some shared fully in planning and doing the work; some were colleagues in foreign lands; some were experimental subjects of early therapeutic trials. So far as possible I shall name them in the pages which follow. Lest any names escape me, I wish to honor them all at this point.

The Fund was established by an agreement, first roughed out in March, 1935 but fully formalized and signed on October 16, 1935 between the three inventors, Robert R. Williams, Robert E. Waterman and Edwin R. Buchman, and Research Corporation. It provided for the outright assignment to Research of all inventions then made or to be made subsequently by the three inventors and their three other associates on the subject of vitamin B_1. It also provided for the diligent prosecution at their own expense of their further studies with the aim of developing a practicable, commercial synthesis of the substance. The agreement recognized the principle that the inventors were entitled to reimbursement for their personal outlays from the earliest receipts of royalties, if any should develop, and to participate in lesser degree in further earnings*.

---

* The inventors and their then associates were to receive out of royalties when, as and if paid to Research, $10,000 reimbursement for expenses incurred during 1935, plus 75 per cent of the first $100,000 of net proceeds and 50 per cent of the second $100,000. Thereafter the inventor group of six members was to receive 25 per cent of net proceeds.

Under the agreement Research Corporation was to retain 25 per cent of all net proceeds to support research in fields of its choice. After reimbursement of the inventors for their expenses, 50 per cent of all earnings were to be placed by Research Corporation in a special fund to be known as the "Williams-Waterman Fund for the Combat of Dietary Diseases."

This Fund, in the words of the agreement, shall be used "for the promotion of such activities as may be deemed useful in combatting dietary diseases or other conditions relating thereto." All expenditures were to be made only on the approval of a Committee set up for that purpose. At the outset the Committee had a membership of five, and later seven or eight. By a formal document of October 31, 1946, the Committee was enlarged to nine members, comprising the three inventor signers of the original agreement, three members designated by Research Corporation and "three additional members chosen (by the six above named) from persons qualified as experts in sciences related to the field of current operation of the Williams-Waterman Fund."

This arrangement, though entered upon with little foreknowledge of the future, has worked well nigh perfectly from an administrative standpoint. No difference has ever arisen within the Committee which did not readily yield to discussion, and no action of importance has ever been taken otherwise than unanimously.

Research Corporation has faithfully fulfilled all of its obligations, has placed full confidence in the Committee and has executed promptly and freely all of the Committee's recommendations. No veto has ever arisen from conflict of authority, and the Corporation has proudly and generously recognized and promoted the province and work of the Fund. Office space and management of accounts and investments have been supplied free of cost, and secretarial and publication services have often been contributed. The relationship has been a completely happy one.

WHETHER TO PATENT

Some words are in order at this point as to why the inventor participation in earnings was set up as it was.

I originally undertook the work without thought of pecuniary return or even any foresight that such a return might ever become possible. The circumstances of this are made clear in Chapter II.

However, by the time we succeeded in isolating the vitamin in August of 1933, it was evident that a commercial interest might well arise and that unless we protected our findings by patents we might find the results used, perhaps in quite selfish ways, by firms having a commercial interest in synthetic vitamin B_1.

Once the late Dr. John C. Merriam, president of Carnegie Institution, who was charged with supervising our use of Carnegie Corporation Funds (see Chapter II) was acquainted with these views, he undertook a series of conferences with his advisors to formulate some policy about the disposition of patent rights—if indeed the patenting of research results obtained by the use of Carnegie money was to be permitted at all.

When no clear decision on these points was forthcoming—after the lapse of 18 months—I and my associates, Waterman and Buchman, decided that further delay was intolerable. Accordingly, on January 26, 1935 I withdrew the request to Carnegie for further support, and we three inventors agreed to finance the work out of our own pockets until some other support could be arranged.

Before learning of Research Corporation and prior to meeting Mr. H. A. Poillon, then its President, I had already approached Rockefeller Foundation, the American Medical Association and others to determine whether these organizations would accept a gift of the projected patents. Since there was no encouragement from these sources, we were delighted to discover Research Corporation whose charter was ideally fitted to our needs. We promptly reached a tentative general understanding with Mr. Poillon.

MORAL OBLIGATIONS TO SOCIETY AND TO FAMILIES

In doing so, Waterman, and I particularly, felt a moral obligation to Carnegie and especially to Dr. Paul Keppel, president of Carnegie Corporation, and to Mr. J. J. Carty, one of their directors, whom we felt had been primarily responsible for getting us important financial assistance over a period of seven years.

We did not wish to profit personally—not even indirectly—from the Carnegie money, which we recognized had been given to advance general welfare. No stipulations about the use of the results had been involved in the Carnegie grants but a general sense of honor called for primary consideration to be given to public benefit from the work.

On the other hand, Waterman for 10 years, and I for 24, had invested thousands of hours each year without compensation. In addition I had paid several hundred dollars a year out of my savings for supplies, equipment and salaries of assistants. This continued even after the Carnegie grants became available. Every year, from 1930 to 1934, there was a delay of one to three months after the previous grant was expended before a renewal was made. In the meantime I always carried the payroll and was not allowed to reimburse myself out of the succeeding grant. Under conditions of the depression this was a serious hardship. Dr. Merriam conformed to standard rules by telling me that "Carnegie money was not to be used to pay for dead horses." Under the circumstances Waterman and I felt obligated in our own interest and that of our families to recoup, if possible, the investments of time and money.

Buchman, a recent recruit, who had not participated in the arrangement with Carnegie, of course, was less bound by this obligation. The arrangement with Research for inventor participation in royalties was the best available compromise of differing views. No one then knew whether royalties of any sort would accumulate. If we had to do it over again I doubt that we could find a better solution. Buchman, though relatively new to the task, was the only one of the group who at that time had a perfected invention of synthesis to his credit, providing him with a basis for a larger participation than otherwise justifiable.

The provision in the agreement for a "Fund for the Combat of Dietary Diseases" was in keeping with the thought that profits, if any, from human dietary misery should go to abolish that misery. More specifically, we had in mind the eradication of beriberi in rice-eating Asia. It was through my introduction to this disease in Manila in 1910 that the entire research had received its impetus. The terms of the agreement were, however, sufficiently broad to cover attacks on all deficiency diseases and to support basic research which might be necessary to disclose fully their causes, and their interrelationships and, in fact, to develop broad knowledge of the dependence of public health on food.

WHY ONE MUST PATENT HIS INVENTIONS

The prime purpose in revealing the following history, some of it unpleasant, is to throw light on how one can best use his own scientific research for the ends which he holds most dear. Our view is that as long as our patent laws exist there is an obligation on every scientific worker to protect his inventions by patents if he can write a truthful and valid application. Protection of the public by mere publication is an unrealistic dream.

Unless the non-patenting inventor gets into print one year before a pirate inventor files his application, there is no provision of law whereby the Patent Office can refuse to credit the pirate's claims. If less than one year has elapsed between prior publication and the filing of the application, the pirate may by statement under oath declare that his discovery or conception antedated the publication. In such a case the non-patenting scientist will have no opportunity to present contrary evidence, as Interferences in the Patent Office are limited to matters of conflict of claims in patent applications which are simultaneously on file in the Patent Office.

Even when the rival inventor has delayed his filing more than one year it is very often possible for him to cover by patent some improvement or betterment or some additional finding which will enable him to capitalize on the whole. Scientific papers do not and should not include legal claims for contemplated inventions as patent applications do of necessity.

The scientific paper may be truly valuable even if it furnishes only a hint or a clue, and it is important for the welfare of science that it be published early but it should not include more than the then known facts. Patent applications are privately filed and may properly include conjecture as well as fact. They may be abandoned or changed before issuance if projected ideas prove false or need to be modified.

Whether or not temporary monopolies to inventors should be provided through issue of patents is a larger question which we will not discuss here. Our belief is that the patent system does promote scientific advance and technological invention by providing a stimulus to invent and especially an incentive to disclose discoveries to the public. Without such a patent law secret processes would be in frequent use and public knowledge of technology would depend on spying. However, we are utterly sympathetic with those who wish the evils of patent law to be corrected. The public interest must always come first. It is quite idle to suppose that one can truly protect the public interest by ignoring the existing patent law.

We think we have shown the way to serve public welfare under existing circumstances. Now in the light of events there can be no doubt that a world monopoly in vitamin B_1 would have wound up in the hands of I. G. Farbengesellschaft had we not persisted in patenting in spite of much opposition and embarrassment from well meaning and public-spirited fellow scientists whose feelings, as well as professional attainments, we honor very highly but whose practical judgment we regard as quite quixotic and ill-informed.

A FINANCIAL SUMMARY

The first accrual in the Fund amounting to $8,226.75 occurred in August, 1939. Since that time the total royalty receipts to October 31, 1955 have reached the sum of $4,070,430.97, supplemented by $447,996.15 of earnings on investments and $29,459.37 of other income. Of the total receipts of $4,547,886.49, there has been appropriated $2,320,817.29 for grants in aid of projects proposed by qualified investigators. In addition, approximately $100,231.51 was spent for projects undertaken by the Fund in its own name. The net expenses of administration have been $164,278.69, or 7.1 per cent of spendings for the stated objectives of the Fund.

The present assets of the Fund, chiefly in securities, had a book value of $1,962,559.00 as of October 31, 1955, not including a non-realized appreciation of investments of $355,754.10. During the remaining life of the patents further income from royalties and investments, added to present reserves, should provide a sum at least equal to what has already been expended. In other words, the life of the Fund is now half spent as far as income from the thiamine patents is concerned.

In retrospect I find this summary of income and outlay very gratifying indeed. I can recall most vividly submitting to my long-time friend and colleague, Robert Waterman, the first draft of the then proposed 1935 agreement in which reference was made to the first and second $100,000 of net proceeds. Waterman, who is always frank and often pithy of speech, dubbed these mythical figures "box-car numbers."

I do not hold this contemptuous comment against Waterman, whose role in our joint undertaking was often that of deflator of high flights of fancy and especially of hopeful interpretations of experimental results which, alas, were too often ambiguous. It must be recalled that at the time of the agreement no method of synthesis existed. Even full details of structure were unknown. There was, of course, no concept of the economics of manufacture nor of the potential market demand. We are fortunate indeed to have had it turn out so fabulously well.

THE COMMITTEE TO ADMINISTER THE FUND

The first meeting of the Committee was held on March 28, 1940. Membership at that time consisted of Dave Hennen Morris, Chairman, Robert E. Waterman, Secretary, Howard A. Poillon, Henry C. Sherman and R. R. Williams.

In 1941 Dr. Norman Jolliffe joined the Committee; in 1942, Dr. Charles Glen King; in 1944, Dr. William Henry Sebrell, Jr. Following the death of Mr. Morris on May 4, 1944 and the initiation of the prolonged illness and incapacitation of Mr. Poillon in the autumn of that year, I succeeded as Chairman in January, 1945, taking over also the responsibility as Secretary from Mr. Waterman, who had recently retired from Research Corporation to become vice president of Schering Corporation.

During 1946 the Committee was expanded and further formalized. Dr. J. W. Barker and Mr. Howard Coonley, together with Mr. C. H. Schauer, who became Secretary, were designated as the Research Corporation representatives. Mr. Waterman, Dr. E. R. Buchman, with Dr. Charles D. Coryell as alternate, and I represented the inventor group, and Doctors Jolliffe, King and Sebrell, the professional public members with Dr. Henry C. Sherman and Dr. Robert R. Williams, Jr. as advisors.

On September 14, 1955 Dr. Sam C. Smith succeeded Mr. C. H. Schauer, as Secretary. We have lost Doctor Sherman by death and the younger Doctor Williams by removal from the New York area. Mr. Schauer has replaced Mr. Coonley. Dr. John C. Keresztesy has been named as alternate to Mr. Waterman. Otherwise, the Committee at the present writing is unchanged.

Above: The author in 1912.

Right: The Williams-Waterman Committee in session, 1956.

Below: A fortunate reunion, March 16, 1956, of nearly all the persons who have been associated with the initial research or with management of the Williams-Waterman Fund.

Top Left: The late Dr. Edward B. Vedder in 1946.

Top Right: Medical Research Institute, Kuala Lumpur, Malaya, the scene of Fraser and Stanton's work.

Center: The Eijkman Institute, Djakarta, where thirty-odd years of pioneering on beriberi was done.

At Right: B. C. P. Jansen, the first to isolate vitamin B_1.

CHAPTER II

The Antecedent Research

Although it does not directly concern the conduct of the Williams-Waterman Fund, a brief account of the antecedent research is of great interest as background. It also gives an opportunity to name and to thank many persons who, in then unforeseeable ways, helped to make the Fund and its work possible. The vicissitudes of fate have made some of these acknowledgments heretofore impossible but have not erased grateful memories from my mind.

It is hoped that an account of this research and how its results have been bent to form a support for further scientific endeavor will be usefully suggestive to other investigators who may feel an impulsion to use their own inventions in concrete ways for public benefit.

We have learned much from practical experience about inventions and patents, how they may be put to work for the public weal, wasted or weakened through neglect of provisions of existing law. We shall be happy to transmit this experience to others so far as such transmission is possible.

BEGINNINGS IN THE ORIENT

I was introduced to the subject of beriberi in Manila in early September, 1910 by the then Captain Edward B. Vedder, U.S. Army Medical Corps. Vedder was a member of the Army Board of Tropical Medicine and was directly concerned with the matter because of the high incidence of incapacitation from duty and of deaths from beriberi among the Philippine Scouts, which at that time was a branch of the U. S. Army.

The whole atmosphere of Manila at the time was pregnant with ideas on this controversial subject. Pasteur's concept that disease is caused by micro-organisms was so recently but so firmly ingrained in nearly all medical minds that few could credit the reports of Eijkman and Grijns from Java that beriberi could be produced in chickens simply by feeding them nothing but white rice.

Confirmatory reports of like results in humans in Malaya had just been presented by Fraser and Stanton at the Annual Congress of Tropical Medicine held in Manila earlier that year.

A number of other researches on beriberi got under way in Manila about that time. Hans Aron, in the organization in which I was a new recruit, The Bureau of Science, was studying the phosphorus content of rice in relation to its beriberi-producing qualities. Manuel Guerrero, Jose Albert, and later Vernon Andrews, pursued the study of taon, dramatically proving it to be the infantile form of beriberi. Richard Strong and B. C. Crowell were producing experimental human beriberi in volunteer prisoners in Bilibid Prison.

Vedder's approach, however, was the most fundamental and ambitious. It concerned nothing less than the isolation and identification of the substance missing from white rice. He brought a liter bottle of rice polish extract to me on his first visit and after reviewing what was already known, he asked me to analyze the extract for all components. Vedder was rather a novice in chemistry at the time and I am sure he had no notion that it would take me 26 years to give him a significant report. I did the chemistry and Vedder did the testing on chickens. Incidentally, his top sergeant in charge of the poultry was none other than the present Prof. W. W. Swingle of Princeton.

Vedder was indefatigable in research throughout his life and had a very fertile mind. After a brief experience at Rockefeller Institute he entered the Army Medical Corps at age 25. Thereafter, at whatever army post he was stationed, often isolated ones, he managed to do some substantial research. A major subject of study for him was syphilis. He also worked on the use of chlorine to control colds and whooping cough. Perhaps the most notable achievement of his later years, one requiring all the great chemical ingenuity which he subsequently developed, was the successful isolation of vitamin C. He was anticipated by a few weeks by the publications of C. G. King and associates but his discovery was independent and significant. Vedder's book, "Beriberi"*, is a critical review of all studies that preceded his. It also gives a good description of his own and other work of that decade. Some account of my early experiences has also been published.**

WORK IN AMERICA, EUROPE AND JAVA

The work in Manila proved that we were dealing with a diffusible, nitrogenous substance of strong basic nature, possessing remarkable prophylactic and curative properties. There followed for me a long period, first in Washington, D. C., later in New Jersey and New York, of confused search for a method of isolation of the substance. The work was taken up by others in France, England, Japan and Germany and was also continuously pursued in Java by Eijkman's successors.

---

* E. B. Vedder, "Beriberi." Wm. Wood, New York (1913).
** R. R. Williams. "Recollections of the Beriberi-Preventing Substance." *Nutrition Reviews* 11, 257 (1953).

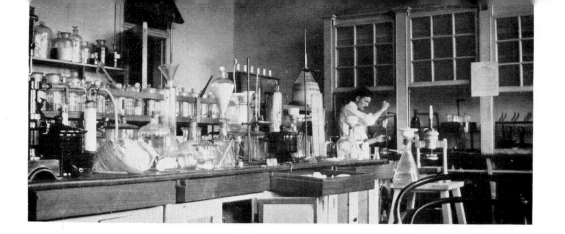

Top: The author in laboratory in 1911.

Center: Bureau of Science, Manila, before wartime destruction.

Bottom: With Secretary of Health, Dr. Paulino Garcia, 1956.

My own greatest difficulty was to produce pure beriberi in experimental animals and disentangle the effects of other B vitamins from those of the "beriberi-preventing substance," which we had come to call vitamin B_1. Accordingly, many years were consumed in trying various species of animals, various diets, and in using successive fractions of rice polish or yeast as curative agents. We had to have some means—at least roughly quantitative—for measuring the distribution of the potent substance among chemical fractions, as well as losses of it by destruction.

We finally resorted to the rat and used a synthetic diet supplemented by autoclaved yeast according to the excellent method suggested by M. I. Smith. This had the advantage of providing a curative test so that by maintaining a colony of rats on the diet it was possible to keep a succession of animals coming into a polyneuritic state and thus get a measure of the activity of any fraction within two or three days. At the same time precision was excellent because the complications of other forms of inanition were avoided.

The first to score a major success were Jansen and Donath in Java in 1926. As test animals they used rice birds which developed polyneuritis so quickly that there was not time for other B deficiencies to build up seriously. By this means they isolated a small fraction of a gram of the crystalline vitamin and analyzed it for carbon, hydrogen and nitrogen. The analysis could not be interpreted rationally as they had completely overlooked the presence of sulphur. A. Windaus, in Germany, demonstrated its presence in the vitamin as isolated from yeast in 1931.

VITAMIN RESEARCH AS AVOCATION

In the meantime I had moved from Manila to Washington, thence to Roselle, New Jersey, where I joined the Western Electric Company, New York to work on the problem of submarine insulation. With the organization of Bell Telephone Laboratories on January 1, 1925, I became its Chemical Director and had a big job on my hands. Nevertheless, at no time since my initiation by Vedder in 1910 did I give up on the vitamin problem, even under pressure of jobs related to World War I. During my Bell System employment I had, at first, assistance grants of a few hundred dollars each from the Fleischmann Company for four or five years. Later, with the aid of Mr. J. J. Carty, Vice President of American Telephone and Telegraph Company and a director of Carnegie Corporation, I secured a grant of $5,000 a year from 1927 to 1933 and $10,000 in 1934 from Carnegie sources. All of these grants were used entirely for purchase of equipment, animals and supplies and for the employment of assistants, often students earning their way through college.

Among others, I employed during odd-hour periods some fellow members of the Bell System staff. One of them was Stanley O. Morgan who has since achieved distinction in dielectrics and in phases of solid state physics. This vitamin job, however, was rather foreign to his interests, and he quit the work when he left Bell to go to graduate school.

In contrast, Robert Waterman, who worked odd times for a dollar an hour at first, soon told me he wanted no further pay. He put his back into the work from 1924 to 1936 and was in at the finish. His greatest virtue was that he steadfastly refused to believe what he would have liked to believe and insisted on proving every point to the hilt. Oh! the arguments we had.

Still another helper in those days was Verne Myers, then a high school boy, who weighed, fed and watered the pigeons at daybreak each morning for several years. The pigeons were kept at my home in the garage in lieu of a Cadillac. With this arrangement I could study the results over my breakfast coffee and decide what preparation we should try to make next in my laboratory in a basement room of New York Hospital. I have forgotten the names of some of the student boys and girls who helped me for brief intervals at that phase of the job. One I remember, but will not mention, had the characteristic of always getting the result which he guessed I would like. We built up a nice house of cards during his incumbency but a breeze of stray truth blew it down after a few months.

NEW RECRUITS AT COLUMBIA UNIVERSITY

As the relatively lush Carnegie funds became available in 1927, Dr. Walter H. Eddy generously put some laboratory space at Teachers College at our disposal and we were able to employ a series of graduate students in chemistry who were not averse to an honest dollar. Among these were Sadie Morris, Celia Zahl, Samuel Gurin, Marion Ammerman and John C. Keresztesy. The last three named saw the isolation work brought to a finish and witnessed a good start made on structure.

For years Waterman and I would commute to Columbia from one to three evenings a week after our day's work at Bell was done. Later, as the depression came and deepened, our work week at Bell was shortened and we had longer and longer week-ends to spend at Columbia. At the worst (or best) we had four, or at least three, out of seven days each week.

At last we reached the stage in isolation where we felt we had a process which would work if applied on a sufficiently large scale. Through Professor Jackson we got the use of the Chemical Engineering Laboratory where we installed a 1300 gallon wooden tank to make the initial extraction. After many vicissitudes we would bring the isolation of the batch to a conclusion ultimately in a 30 cc. test tube over at Teachers College. Professor Hixon, who had direct charge of the laboratory in Havemeyer Hall, was a stickler for rules. We recall with extreme gratitude the kindlier disposition of Associate Professor Lincoln T. Work who would

Top: Tank for initial extraction of rice polish.

Center: Successful isolation, 1933.

Bottom: Reunion of researchers, 1956. Gurin, Major, Williams, Celia Zahl Gurin, Cline, Clarke, Marion Ammerman Keresztesy, Keresztesy, Buchman, Waterman. Only Jacob Finkelstein was absent.

often slip us a key on the sly for out-of-hours visits to Chemical Engineering.

We tried in vain to repeat Jansen and Donath's procedure of producing crystals but our results on the distribution of activity in the fractions tended to confirm their claims. A visit to Jansen's laboratory in Amsterdam in 1929 had quite convinced me that they actually had small amounts of the pure or nearly pure substance in crystalline form.

SUCCESS IN ISOLATION AND THE SULFITE CLEAVAGE

Therefore we set out upon the task, as indicated above, of obtaining better yields of the substance so as to have enough to study its chemistry. We succeeded in July, 1933 by our own method in obtaining 20 times better yields from rice polish principally by reducing the extent of destruction in releasing the vitamin from fuller's earth.

Within a few weeks we had a gram of crystals in hand and seriously set about study of structure. The very first experiment we did was highly successful. On the basis of my recollection from years before that all activity had disappeared overnight in yeast extract which I had tried to preserve with sulfite against bacterial action, we tried sulfite on the pure vitamin. In neutral solution we got quantitative yields of an insoluble crystalline solid (the pyrimidine in the form of a sulfonic acid as we learned later) and a chloroform extractable oil, which proved to be a thiazole.

ENTER DR. H. T. CLARKE

At this juncture I needed the assistance of someone much better versed in systematic structural chemistry than myself. So I formed an alliance about September 1, 1933 with Dr. Hans Thacher Clarke of Columbia University Medical School. Dr. Clarke was for some months quite skeptical that we had the vitamin in a pure state. He enlisted Dr. Oskar Wintersteiner and Mr. W. Saschek in a series of analyses after successive recrystallizations. Difficulty was encountered in obtaining consistent nitrogen determinations and this accentuated Dr. Clarke's suspicions. Later, we found that in the course of analysis the pyrimidine portion of the molecule is difficult to decompose completely. This caused us a great deal of trouble and delay in later stages of the work as well.

Dr. Clarke was even more skeptical of the unconventional approach we had made to the subject by the use of sulfite cleavage. Six months had now elapsed since my first approach to Dr. Clarke and he had not yet found a student of his own choice to devote full time to the structure studies. We knew we were in a race with Windaus and presumably other Germans. In desperation I enlisted Dr. Edwin R. Buchman in April, 1934 to assist us at Teachers College where Waterman and I were working with Marion Ammerman and John C. Keresztesy as student assistants. This was done without the approval of Dr. Clarke and it caused the first rift in our relations.

A further rift, amounting to almost complete rupture, developed when we told Dr. Clarke that we proposed to patent our procedures in so far as they appeared to have possible commercial value. Dr. Clarke's position was that no patent has any proper place in a program of medical research. He apparently regarded patents as antisocial and a prostitution of scientific skills.

Thereafter, the collaboration broke down and became a process of picking up the pieces and allocating credits in as amicable a manner as possible. In this process I had the unenviable task of allaying ill will and suspicion between the groups and getting the job done somehow. I gained a great advantage in that Dr. Samuel Gurin, previously my assistant and associate in developing isolation procedures, had become a trusted pupil and associate of Dr. Clarke. As a good friend of both of us, he must have done much to smooth over difficulties. In addition, to the best of my knowledge and belief, it was Gurin who by a search of the literature first made the surmise that the sulphur of the vitamin is in thiazole form.

THE THIAZOLE SYNTHESIS

Dr. Buchman, a very able young organic chemist, attacked the job with vigor and skill. Largely through his work, but with the aid of several others, the structure of the sulphur-containing moiety was not only determined but also verified by a complete synthesis prior to March, 1935.

In so doing he violated, I fear, some of the understandings I had with Clarke's group about division of responsibilities between the groups. The job was done, however, and could not be undone so Waterman and I had to deal with the task not in the way we would have preferred but in the only way that offered.

After another three months, Buchman, pleading ill health, left us. He later went to Johns Hopkins where, after some months, he resumed work on better methods of thiazole synthesis. Buchman assigned his inventions to Research Corporation and paid his share of current expenses in accordance with an agreement reached in the early months of 1935 with Waterman and myself.

I still cannot explain Buchman's leaving. Conjecture would be idle. It left Waterman and me, neither of us very skilled in systematic organic chemistry, to make what progress we could in our odd moments during the summer and early fall of 1935. Fortunately, we did have the help of Jacob Finkelstein who had been enlisted early in the year as an assistant to Buchman. He was engaged in an extensive program of preparation of pyrimidine derivatives which we felt we would need for comparative purposes.

This pyrimidine program was rendered vastly more useful by the ultra-violet absorption spectra taken for us by A. E. Ruehle, a Bell Laboratories chemist, who undertook all this as a labor of love in his leisure hours of the depression period. In emergencies these leisure hours, the reader may be sure, were not very leisurely.

Waterman and I did achieve during the summer a new cleavage of the vitamin in liquid ammonia from which we isolated 2-methyl, 6-amino, 5-aminomethyl pyrimidine. This substance proved of great importance patentwise, though we did not prove its structure until several months later. Otherwise, this cleavage was not very revealing since there were various by-reactions leading to a mixture of products.

MERCK & CO. ENLISTED THROUGH DR. RANDOLPH T. MAJOR

We had long ago—in early 1934—approached Dr. Randolph T. Major of Merck & Co., Inc. to get his firm's assistance in the early large-scale operations of extracting the vitamin from rice polish. We got a cordial welcome and later transferred Keresztesy to the Merck payroll to supervise that operation.

Early in 1935 we tendered our embryonic invention to Research Corporation. In return, we hoped for financial assistance in carrying the job through to a conclusion. Here, too, we had a cordial welcome. But Research Corporation was very hard up at the end of the depression and was living on its reserves from the 1920's, so we had to continue supporting the research ourselves.

In the meantime Mr. Poillon, the President of Research Corporation, sought to reach an agreement whereby Merck would pay in advance for royalties on yet unborn inventions. This took many months to negotiate and it was not until October 16, 1935 that Waterman, Finkelstein and I moved into two laboratories at Merck's Rahway plant which were set aside for our use.

There we had the use of Merck's stockroom, library, their excellent and indispensable microanalytical laboratory, and abundant animal facilities. I had full charge of the job and met with cordial help from the Merck staff on demand, all in a very satisfactory manner. The facilities were vastly superior to any we had heretofore for synthetic work. Most important of all, we were assigned the help from Merck's staff of a talented young organic chemist, Joseph K. Cline, who made invaluable contributions to the identification and synthesis of the pyrimidine portion, which was the principal unfinished task. He also shared in the final condensation which gave us curative, synthetic reaction mixtures and presently crystals in abundance.

In retrospect it is a great pity that we could not have retained Buchman's services, or have had Cline's services six months earlier. It might have brought our work to a conclusion more promptly and would have served to establish valid patent rights throughout the world. As the event proved, we established rights of substantial value only in the United States and Canada, and to a very limited extent in Germany.

Cline had one serious fault: he would not stop his laboratory work long enough to write up his notes. In the end, this almost cost us our shirts, but fortunately not quite.

THE SHOWDOWN WITH I. G.

Although the essential research was concluded by June, 1936, the issue of patent protection was not settled until March 2, 1942. Within a few weeks of our published announcement of the synthesis in June, 1936, Dr. Heinrich Hoerlein of I. G. Farbengesellschaft came to the United States to investigate. He told Mr. Poillon that his firm had the synthesis of vitamin B_1 all sewed up but generously offered to consider some concession to Research Corporation as assignee in view of Williams' contributions to the structure, if Mr. Poillon would lay all his cards on the table.

Mr. Poillon, through some process of divination of which only he was capable and without his consulting anyone else, told Dr. Hoerlein that he was not interested. A highly indignant Dr. Hoerlein was forced to make the reverse journey across the Atlantic to report a futile conversation of five minutes' duration.

The patent records of Germany and England subsequently showed a series of patent applications by I. G. beginning in March, 1935. All of these up to the end of that year faithfully reflected the faults of the structure published by Williams as the probable one in January, 1935. Antineuritic properties were attributed to scores of named substances, none of which possesses any. By group claims such properties were attributed to some hundreds more. It is evident that I. G. began filing by guess a year before they knew the true structure and, of course, their applications included predictions of reactions which would have worked if they had known to what compounds they should be applied to obtain physiological activity.

We filed on the synthesis of the thiazole portion as soon as we knew its structure and Buchman had made it. We delayed filing on the pyrimidine portion and on its condensation with the thiazole until we had actually cured rats of polyneuritis with a synthetic product.

As a result, we were far behind the Germans in filing on both of the two general type reactions by which thiamine has since been made, though we had them both in our minds and in our notes for months before we found out which pyrimidine would yield the true vitamin. Here we had been faced with a nice problem in legal scientific ethics. It would have been an enormous advantage to file on conjecture but we preferred to run the risk of waiting to prove our case.

Of course, we were presently thrown into interference in the United States Patent Office with Andersag and Westphal, the German inventors. However, we had the great advantage of being able to submit evidence from our notebooks and records because we were United States' citizens; the Germans, as foreigners, had to rely solely on their filing date in the German patent office. This date we anticipated by prior record of correct conception in our notebooks. Hence Andersag and Westphal were forced to concede, through their attorneys, our priority on all the more essential claims. It was in this way that the matter was at last settled.

In England, Continental Europe and Asia we obtained only very partial protection.

CHAPTER III

Contributions of the Fund
to Advance of Science

The first meeting of the Fund was held on March 28, 1940 when for the first time we had some money to spend. An early decision in which the Committee participated was whether to spend the Fund as it accumulated or to invest a substantial part of our income to extend our activities beyond the life of the patents.

The decision was to spend rather than to conserve for the future. This was dictated in part by the preference of the inventor group and in part by the corporate status of Research Corporation as a tax-exempt foundation whose position might be questioned if it made accumulation for the future a major objective. Our scientific advisors also felt that the then urgent needs for nutritional research and dietary reforms were as great as they were likely to be some decades later.

Actually, as the United States became involved in the war and its scientific personnel became absorbed in war activities, it was impossible to spend our income fruitfully for lack of qualified personnel with free time to give to work of peacetime character. The war years, therefore, automatically became a period of accumulation. In retrospect, this is fortunate on the whole for it will extend beneficially the life of the Fund beyond the life of the patents but will avoid creation of a monument to its founders.

The appraisal of the value of the research programs which the Fund has aided had best be left largely to a future generation who will have better perspective. Since that generation, however, will feel that it has more useful and urgent things to do, we shall take a modest and tentative look at their values. Mostly, however, we shall content ourselves with summarizing only major points of what has been attempted and what has been learned.

As a man who has earned a livelihood by doing and directing research through most of my life, I realize as well as anyone that disappointments, delays and ambiguities of results are the daily bread of the researcher.

Truly, the researcher is mostly engaged in trying again. He sees "color" every few days or few weeks—but usually the "color" soon runs out. He strikes real "pay dirt" only once a year, once a decade or once in a lifetime. Sometimes, unhappily, he never strikes it. All research must be judged as a chancy gamble.

It is also true that well conducted research builds up through the years. The researcher is always learning something—if not necessarily the thing he set out to learn. If he is lucky and discerning, the unexpected discovery may prove to be far more important than his original objective and may start him off on a new and fruitful course. Usually, however, his task is to make careful note of each item he learns and to try later to make sense of a series of observations which may at first have seemed unrelated.

Often this synthesis by intercomparison will also involve the work of another, perhaps many others. It was Irving Langmuir, more than anyone else of my acquaintance, who emphasized that every experiment has some meaning if one can ferret it out. It is thus that science grows. We shall try to judge the work of our grantees in a broad-minded way.

THE FIRST GRANTS

One of the two grants made at the Fund's first meeting in 1940 was for the work of Dr. Tom D. Spies in combatting nutritional disease at Birmingham. Throughout the later years there has been a continuous series of grants for the work of the same man at Cincinnati, Birmingham, Chicago and Havana, the stated purposes having varied somewhat from time to time. The theme which has most prevailed, however, has been the training of young doctors in the recognition and treatment of metabolic diseases.

Perhaps the grants should therefore be classed as education rather than research. Nevertheless, it is recognized that Dr. Spies' great impact upon the medical profession's interest in nutritional disease might have been slight had it not been for his successes in medical research. His initial successful treatment of pellagra with nicotinic acid was already done before we had money to give. We have not hesitated, however, to aid him in capitalizing on his earlier fame. Our total contribution to his work has been $101,000 through December 31, 1955.

The other of the first two grants went to Johns Hopkins University for the work of Dr. E. V. McCollum on vitamin E. It has been our privilege to aid briefly two other of Professor McCollum's undertakings in subsequent years.

In this history I shall make no attempt to go systematically through the projects supported or aided. Rather, I shall choose a few major and more continuous researches, recognizing that in this manner I may omit all special mention of something which the future may prove the most significant act of the Fund. I profess no prophetic powers.

A complete list of all research projects aided appears at the end of this book. Wiser heads may thus discern our better and worse bets for themselves.

SOME MAJOR PROJECTS

A long continued research interest of the Fund has been in the work of Dr. Grace A. Goldsmith at Tulane University under the general heading of "Clinical Investigation of Nutritional Diseases." This work has had our support from 1945 up to the present in the total amount of $88,500, and has embraced a variety of subjects.

Some of the outstanding ones are: the quantitative human requirement for niacin as affected by major components of diet (the lower limit is about 0.1 mg. per kilo of body weight); dissipation of human pellagric lesions by the use of tryptophan; the significance of urinary excretions of the B vitamins and their metabolic derivatives; the inadequacies in pregnancy of low-income Louisiana diets; the merit of skim milk in school lunch programs for children of that area; etiology and treatment of glossitis; procedures for diagnosis of beriberi heart disease; interrelationships among folic acid, folinic acid, vitamin C and vitamin B_{12} in normal persons. In summary, the main aim has been the transfer from experimental animals to humans of our knowledge of the role of B vitamins in metabolism.

Apart from the above project which has been the chief undertaking for which Dr. Goldsmith has asked aid, she was enlisted most fruitfully in a nutritional survey at Norris Point, Newfoundland in 1944 and a resurvey in 1948. These surveys will be mentioned again in Chapter V, page 54. At our request she has also furnished training and experience for Miss Leticia R. Mendiola, a Filipina, and for Dr. Po-Chao Huang, a Formosan, during the past year in her laboratories.

Two related projects for which Dr. Ruth F. Harrell was largely responsible may be mentioned together. The first concerned the effect on their learning ability of additions of thiamine to the diets of children; the second dealt with the relation of pre-natal diets to the mentality of the young. Each of these studies has been published as a monograph*.

The subject of the relation of nutrition, and especially of pre-natal nutrition to mental ability, is one of vast potential importance. In the human it presents great difficulty for its proper study, therefore these

---

* Ruth F. Harrell. "Further Effects of Added Thiamine on Learning and other Processes." Contribution to Education No. 298. Teachers College, Columbia University, New York (1947).
Ruth F. Harrell, Ella Woodyard and Arthur I. Gates. "The Effect of Mothers' Diets on the Intelligence of Offspring." Teachers College, Columbia University, New York (1955).

Top: Dr. Grace A. Goldsmith.

Center: East Newfoundland Survey party.

Bottom: Stern West Coast of Newfoundland near Norris Point.

monographs can only be regarded as a suggestive beginning. The Fund has contributed $42,000 to these studies.

Another of the rather long-term contributions of the Fund went to the work of the late Dr. Burt S. Wolbach from 1947 to 1954, totaling $32,393. Dr. Wolbach supported from personal sources the major part of the studies which he undertook on an emeritus status at Children's Hospital, Boston. Our aid was designed to evoke for public benefit the fruits of a long experience and diminish the burden on him.

He established at Children's Hospital the Division of Nutritional Research to provide training in nutrition for young doctors of resident status. The researches conducted by this group dealt mostly with the effect of nutrients on skeletal development. The pathology of vitamin A deficiency and of hypervitaminosis A received careful study which uncovered new aspects of the biochemistry and physiology of bone and cartilage. Changes in blood chemistry and in other tissues which accompany these conditions and their therapy were also described.

In cooperation with Dr. D. M. Hegsted of Harvard, the distinctive histological features accompanying perosis in chicks as a result of either choline or manganese deficiency were defined.

SOME DEPARTURES FROM THE CENTRAL THEME

Two other contributions of the Fund should be mentioned because (1) they were related and substantial and because (2) they represent perhaps the most radical departure from the strict field of work of the Fund which has yet been recorded.

They are the projects of Dr. George W. Kidder, Amherst College, "Metabolic Inhibitors as Chemotherapeutic Agents in the Control of Cancer and Viral Invasions," and of Dr. Gilbert L. Woodside, "Chemotherapeutic Studies on Cancer in Mice."

These projects jointly received $84,787 from the Fund, plus an equal amount of Research Corporation's general funds during the 1949-1951 period.

This work had its genesis in a previous study by Kidder of the relationship of niacin to tryptophan in Tetrahymena. Unlike the rat and the chick, this organism does not synthesize niacin from tryptophan. In the course of this work it was observed that Tetrahymena is unable to synthesize guanine and that certain other purines have powerful inhibitory effects on the guanine enzyme systems. Such an inhibitor was also found to retard completely the growth of certain cancers in mice, but no marked inhibition has yet been shown in any human cancer of the very limited number on which it has been tried.

The whole promise of this new approach to cancer has accordingly faded, and support by the Fund has been discontinued. The idea is, however, still kept in mind and referred to in the literature by numerous investigators of cancer. It may yet prove of major value.

Another project that may be mentioned because it was something of a departure from usual practice was a grant to aid Dr. R. F. Dawson, first of Princeton and later Columbia, to determine whether the nicotinic acid content of corn can be controlled by genetic means.

The answer is clearly in the affirmative. There is no doubt that varieties of corn can be bred which will not produce pellagra in whatever volume they are consumed. However, farmers grow corn for yield of grain. Further, the adaptability of the seed which they plant to the soil and climate, as well as the ability of different varieties to resist diseases and pests, etc. are very complicated matters indeed. All of these have to be solved for each country more or less uniquely. If we had a few more millions of dollars and good persuasive powers, pellagra might ultimately be wiped out in that way. It is not under present circumstances an immediately available measure.

EDUCATIONAL UNDERTAKINGS

The Fund has aided over the years about 230 projects, if one includes a few undertakings in its own name. Of these, more than 200 have been in the United States, and, with the exception of 13, have been research projects.

The exceptions include 10 corn enrichment demonstration projects in five Southern states, totaling $203,680; support of the work of the Food and Nutrition Board 1945-1955, totaling $67,500; limited publication aid to American Public Health Association and financial relief for the New York City Nutrition Council.

These 13 must be classed under the headings of education and public relations rather than research. Also, it should be noted that the mere counting of projects does not correctly reveal the efforts expended in different ways. The expense of our demonstration projects has on the average been much larger than that of most of our single research projects.

APPRAISAL OF RESEARCH REQUIRES PERSPECTIVE OF TIME

Nevertheless it is true, on the whole, that the knowledge which has come from the research which we have helped to support does not overwhelm the casual observer with its magnitude or importance. But at the same time we doubt that our batting average is worse than that of other granting agencies.

Research is expensive, its success is a gamble and its overall worth is difficult to weigh. Viewed piece by piece it may seem rather insignificant. It requires a broad view and prophetic vision to appraise it soundly.

An example from personal experience may be pertinent. When Woh-mann in 1890 recorded the properties of 4-methyl thiazole, 5-carboxylic acid which he had made by a new but unrevolutionary synthesis, he probably thought he was merely adding three lines to Beilstein. Yet, in late 1934, when Sam Gurin was looking for compounds of the composition of the oxidation product of one cleavage product of vitamin B_1, there it was. Wohmann's record of it probably saved us some years of further research on the structure of the vitamin. Similarly, we hope that a large percentage of the findings of our research grantees will ultimately bring an abundant fruition.

Some of our earlier grants, though small in total amount, have already ripened into specific usefulness. One of these, begun by R. S. Harris at Massachusetts Institute of Technology, was at first concerned with evaluation of various techniques for the determination of thiamine; also of various instruments then offered for the purpose. This phase of the project was associated with a Vitamin Assay Conference held by the Fund late in 1940. (See page 47.)

As the selected methods reached reliability, they were used to determine the daily doses of thiamine required by pregnant women as disclosed by tissue saturation above which excessive spillage in the urine occurred. The essential conclusion was that the requirement in late pregnancy is about 3 times higher than in non-pregnant women. The general finding has since been confirmed by others. It bears out the principle, long accepted in the Philippines, that child-bearing women as well as their young infants constitute the group which is most vulnerable to beriberi.

Another early grant, 1940-1943, was for the work of Herbert Pollack at Mt. Sinai Hospital, New York, which concerned the excretion of thiamine and its degradation products. It gave rise to the load test, which has proved quite useful in clinical diagnoses, and it also called attention to excretion of the dissociated pyrimidine moiety of thiamine, a phenomenon which still engages interest and needs further interpretation. This study, like many others of that period, was interrupted by Dr. Pollack's call to military duty.

Another grant to Harvard for Joseph W. Ferrebee in 1941-42 gave us our earliest data on concentration of thiamine in human tissues as affected by dietaries and by concurrent disease. It also provided a method for thiamine assays of biopsy specimens.

A group of diligent workers, directly concerned with experimental methods, could doubtlessly cite a score of the early projects which have furnished data or methods which have subsequently proved useful for further studies. Those of us who run as we read are scarcely qualified to appraise the worth of undramatic details recorded in the literature.

APPLIED NUTRITION

In keeping with the broad purpose of the Fund, as stated in its name, the Committee has always given preference to projects for the application of scientific knowledge to the early betterment of human feeding, or to the correction or prevention of nutritional disease.

Occasionally, a disappointed applicant has criticized our "shortsighted practicality" as he saw it. On the whole, however, the scientific community has evinced a strong sympathy with our point of view. We live in a world undergoing revolutionary changes and unless we can rapidly apply our modern science and technology to better the lot of hundreds of millions of less privileged races, our entire civilization is in danger of being overwhelmed by the envious masses who now realize too little of its benefits.

Unfortunately, the number and variety of truly practical projects which have come to us have been all too meager. Vast undertakings for the betterment of agriculture in various countries have been contemplated. All appeared to be either of restricted significance, of the nature of local relief expeditions, or else they required funds in the hundreds of millions to give them effect. A few projects in clinical surveys and in cereal enrichment endeavors have appeared useful and within our means.

An important outgrowth of corn enrichment in the United States (see pages 54-57) has been a trial of corn enrichment in one area of Yugoslavia, on a demonstration basis, under the leadership of Dr. W. J. Darby of Vanderbilt University and under the auspices of W.H.O. Using feeders and premix obtained from Dr. E. J. Lease of Clemson, corn enrichment has been provided for 17 small mills within a narrow area. Preliminary surveys showed an extensive incidence of severe pellagra, which records indicated had recurred every spring in some families for as long as 15 years. Other surveys, two years later, showed a marked decrease in number and severity of pellagra cases, and this decrease correlated well with the use of enriched corn meal.

Yugoslavia appears to be one of few areas in the world where corn consumption is high, where pellagra is rife, and where production in power driven mills prevails. It is disappointing that so far the Yugoslavian government has taken no definite steps to support extension of corn enrichment to other corn-eating areas. The eradication of pellagra should be quite simple and very cheap.

OUR FOCUS TURNS ABROAD

The Committee has, however, continued to feel the moral pressure to live up to the Fund's name. Hence it has turned its attention increasingly in recent years to situations abroad where nearly all of the world's acute food problems lie.

Our concern abroad has had four principal aspects: (1) early practical measures of food betterment (largely through food enrichment); (2) research, there on the scene, related to indigenous problems; (3) appraisals of existing nutritional status as a basis for future action; and (4) the training of nationals as scientists.

Our experience has been extremely educational for us. Food enrichment programs such as are practical and expeditious here encounter vast difficulties in less developed countries. Of these, the dollar shortage is most severe and widespread. Research undertakings in such countries also present problems: first, inadequacies of trained personnel and of facilities; and second, a rather surprising disposition among many foreign scientists to copy the ivory towers of Western academic learning rather than to address themselves to the acute problems that lie all around them. This is especially true of India; it is not true of Japan.

Appraisals of nutritional status are often troublesome because most of the available physicians do not recognize nutritional disease symptoms. More of this later. The training of nationals in nutritional aspects of medicine, in biochemistry, dietetics, governmental functions in public health, in concepts or plans of effective attack on indigenous problems has unlimited possibilities. We could spend ten times the money we have in these fields alone. The results would not be rapid; perhaps they would be reasonably sure in the long run.

We are still in process of discovering the most useful application of our all too slender funds. Of one thing we have come to feel certain, namely, that the focus of principal future research must be abroad rather than in the United States.

We have made a beginning, largely for experience, by aiding 17 foreign projects with research objectives in less developed areas: 4 in India, 1 each in Pakistan, New Caledonia, the Philippines, Guatemala, Yugoslavia and South Africa, 2 each in Formosa, Cuba and Chile and 1 minor contribution in Brazil.

With the exception of Pakistan, Yugoslavia, South Africa and New Caledonia all of the sites of these researches, as well as many other countries, were visited in search of persons, institutions and locales for such work. In each country visited the applicability and feasibility of food enrichment programs were evaluated as far as possible. By lectures and conferences with nationals, often with participation of officers of United States' missions for foreign aid, the possibilities of cereal enrichment for the country concerned have been portrayed.

The countries visited for these purposes, in addition to those mentioned above, have been: Burma, Thailand, Indonesia, Vietnam, Japan, Mexico, Costa Rica, Panama, Colombia, Ecuador, Peru, Argentina,

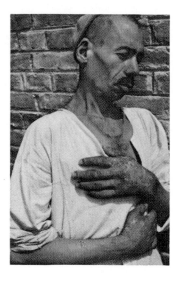

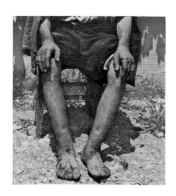

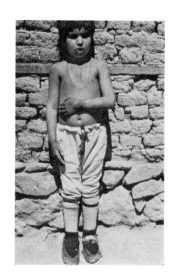

Classical symptoms of pellagra are abundant in mountain valleys of southern Yugoslavia.

India

Above: Nutrition laboratory, Women's Christian College, Madras.

Left: Sundararajan, Mrs. Patwardhan, Williams, Subba Rao, Patwardhan, Coonoor, India.

Below Left: Dr. and Mrs. A. Sreenivasan of Bombay.

Below Right: Expressing sesame oil, India.

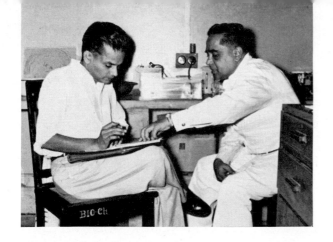

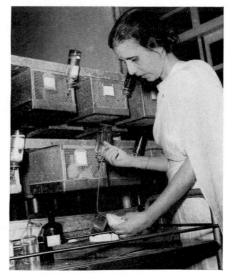

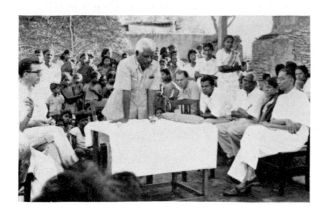

India

Top: Dr. Sreenivasan and Dr. Appana, Vellore, India.

Just Below: District Welfare Officer presides at a village nutrition meeting.

Above Right: Miss Prema Fatterpaker force feeds experimental rat.

Below Right: Mr. J. M. Noronha at Warburg apparatus.

Uruguay and Venezuela. In several of the Latin-American countries a start has been made toward flour or bread enrichment programs. Only in Chile has flour enrichment been established on a firm and substantially universal basis.

Of the foreign research projects above mentioned only a few have advanced sufficiently to permit appraisal of future success or promise. Progress of several of them has been exceedingly slow and discouraging if viewed in the light of the enormous tasks ahead. Some of them have, frankly, been aimed primarily at the further development of the better minds encountered in the country for the sake of present and future leadership. Every one of them has been successful in some degree in this respect.

The undertaking most advanced and assured of success is in Guatemala where Dr. N. S. Scrimshaw has long been established and where our contribution was merely a further and lesser source of funds for an already fruitful program.

The prime objective of the particular work we have aided there is to clarify an apparent discrepancy in our theories of the etiology of pellagra. The association of high corn consumption with the incidence of pellagra was established long ago in Italy and has found further confirmation in southern United States, Roumania, Yugoslavia and Egypt. This accords with our knowledge of the low niacin content of corn. However, in Guatemala and Mexico where corn consumption is exceedingly high, pellagra is rare and mild. There is presumably some other factor in the diets of these areas which affords protection. It has been surmised that the use of lime in the preparation of corn for tortillas, a general practice in these areas but not elsewhere, has something to do with it. This at the moment is not substantiated and the true reason is still unknown. Progress is being made in learning the total niacin and tryptophan intakes, and an answer will probably be forthcoming within a few years. Dr. Grace Goldsmith is collaborating with Scrimshaw in some of the work.

Three other somewhat interrelated projects are fairly certain of producing significant values in a few years. One of these is under Dr. A. Sreenivasan at the University of Bombay and deals with the better utilization of the essential amino acids in Indian dietaries.

Another, under the South Pacific Commission at New Caledonia with Mr. F. E. Peters as leader, is attempting to analyze the proteins of the foods of that area with a view to determining shortages of certain of the amino acids and means of securing better balance in the diets.

A third, a joint project of the Institute of Nutrition, Manila and the University of the Philippines, attempts to do likewise for the foods of that area. The respective leaders are Drs. C. R. Pascual and A. Tenmatay.

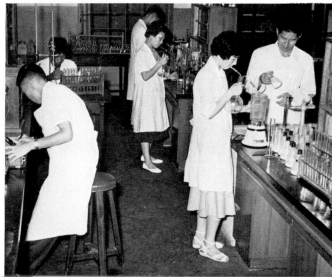

Formosan Survey

Top: Dr. Jolliffe examines boys.

Right: Biochemical analyses, National Taiwan University.

Below Left: Chinese ophthalmologist at work.

Below Right: Dr. Ta-Cheng Tung (center) and associates.

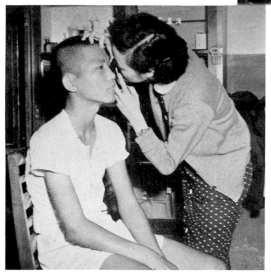

Each of these three projects has very competent leadership and adequate resources of personnel and equipment. The promise of useful information is excellent, but they have been in progress for only short periods as yet.

SURVEYS OF NUTRITIONAL STATUS

Three kindred projects in the nature of clinical surveys of nutritional status are best mentioned together. One of these by Dr. Herbert Pollack concerned the Chinese Nationalist troops in Formosa. Our Fund was concerned only with the initiation of this study. It has been followed much further under the auspices of the United States Department of Defense, Dr. Pollack continuing to furnish guidance of the study.

Another survey in Formosa has been done by Dr. Norman Jolliffe and has concerned the civilian population. Samples were taken chiefly—but not exclusively—from sixth grade school children. Soldiers and civilians showed the same deficiencies, that of riboflavin being most marked and affecting about 75 per cent of persons examined*. Riboflavin intake will apparently be impossible to bring up to the high level of United States standards except by artificial food fortification. Rice enrichment, including riboflavin, will be fairly easy for troops as the cooks can be instructed to cook rice in a way to conserve the vitamins. For civilians this will be impossible immediately as the two prevailing methods of cooking rice will either produce spots of bright yellow color in the cooking pot from localized riboflavin or result in discard of a large part of the added vitamins in excess cooking water.

A clinical survey in Cuba is being conducted among Cuban civilians by Doctors Jolliffe and Goodhart. Almost nothing is known as to prevailing deficiencies in Cuba, and lack of homogeneity of dietary habits in different parts of the Island, plus low school attendance in the fifth and sixth grades, may make sampling of the population far more difficult than in Formosa. It is believed, however, that the clinical survey will prove both more expeditious and informative than did a previous attempt with our support at a dietary survey under Miss Emma Reh of F.A.O. Collection and compilation of data about the amounts of different foods eaten by families, with subsequent calculation of intake of nutrients, appears to give results more indirect and more uncertain than do clinical observations, and the process is slow and laborious. Dietary surveys can be done with less highly skilled persons. However, more persons are needed and they do need to be carefully trained and supervised to secure consistent and reasonably reliable data.

Both in Formosa and in Cuba many young doctors have taken part in

---

* The entire May issue of *Metabolism 5*, 202-358 (1956) is devoted to 17 publications on these surveys.

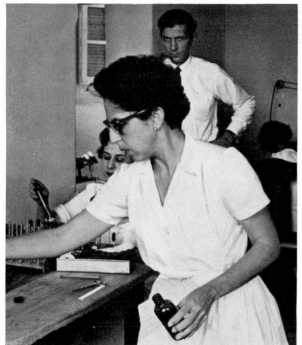

Clinical Survey in Cuba

Above: Examining stations at a school.

Left: Dra. Hady Lopez, Dra. Margarita Cimadevilla (seated), Dr. Kenneth H. Shull.

Bottom: Drs. Van Itallie, Chandrapananda (Thailand) and Goodhart examine boy.

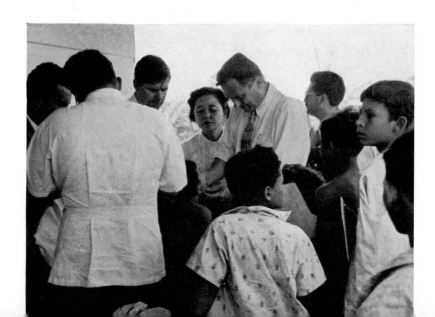

the surveys and have been schooled in the recognition of symptoms and the interpretation of findings. It is believed this will be important for future progress in the betterment of nutrition in both islands.

A further contribution by the Fund to nutritional welfare in Cuba has been to supply a goodly quota of laboratory equipment for both food and clinical analyses at Finlay Institute, Havana, under the auspices of a volunteer civic organization, *Fundacion de Investigaciones Medicas,* led by Mrs. Louise F. Smith, and including many public-spirited residents, both Cuban and American. Dr. Robert S. Harris of Massachusetts Institute of Technology contributes his services as scientific advisor of the Laboratories. The active staff is entirely Cuban and is headed by Dra. Hady Lopez. Great progress has already been made in the analysis of Cuban foods for the chief nutrients of importance. It is hoped that this undertaking will ultimately grow into a broad institute of nutrition with liberal support from the Cuban government. Cuba has indeed been the beneficiary of larger sums from the Fund (total approximately $130,000) than any other foreign country, except the Philippine Republic. The failure, to date, of the development of systematic governmental support in Cuba for nutritional betterment of its people has been a disappointment.

Discussion of our quite important project on kwashiorkor in South Africa will be reserved for Chapter VII.

CHAPTER IV

Cereal Enrichment
Its Effect on the Fund

The first concrete mention of the possible addition of vitamin B_1 to white flour that I know of was made by James F. Bell, then president of General Mills, Inc. and a director of the American Telephone and Telegraph Company. Presumably because of this latter connection Mr. Bell approached me through the late Dr. Frank B. Jewett, then president of the Bell Telephone Laboratories, in which organization I was employed. This was early in 1935. Mr. Bell was told that the vitamin as prepared from natural sources was far too expensive for consideration for this purpose but that a possible synthesis was contemplated. He was promised information if success was achieved and the promise was fulfilled early in 1937.

The Committee on Foods of the American Medical Association (later the Council on Foods and Nutrition) gave its sanction on March 12, 1936 to addition of vitamins and minerals to foods under appropriate restrictions. Then in December, 1938 the Council on Foods and Nutrition and the Council on Chemistry and Pharmacy jointly approved standardized fortification of certain foods among which flour was specifically mentioned. Further action by the Council on Foods in March, 1939 and a meeting of the American Institute of Nutrition in Toronto on April 26, 1939 encouraged still more discussion of the subject.

The event which brought matters to a head however, and which furnished a continuing and vigorous support for bread and flour enrichment, was the establishment of the Committee on Food and Nutrition (which later became the Food and Nutrition Board) late in 1940 under the vigorous leadership of Dr. Russell M. Wilder, with influential assistance from Dr. M. L. Wilson and others. Leading millers, acting through the Millers' National Federation, as well as many large bakers representing the American Bakers Association, with the scientific collaboration of the American Institute of Baking, were favorable to the idea or at least keenly interested.

Food and Nutrition Board, 1944

About table, left to right: Boudreau, Wilder, Black, Cowgill, McCollum, Longenecker, Gunderson, Gortner, Maynard, Williams, Tisdall, Murlin, Prescott, Sherman; (Second row) Griggs, Sebrell, Hall, Mitchell, Frey, Davis; (continuing at right) Stanley, Hoobler, Jeans, Pett, Elvehjem, Nelson; (Outer row) Kruse, Youmans, Jolliffe, Bulman, Stiebeling, Sydenstricker, Bing, Rose.

Such industry support was a very large factor in later success. The Food and Drug Administration was highly cooperative and reopened the public hearings on definitions and standards of identity for flour. A foundation was thus laid for the whole cereal enrichment program which has ensued. The rather complex history of this movement is outlined elsewhere*. Suffice it to say here that by early 1943, 70 per cent of the white flour and bread was being enriched. It has since advanced to perhaps 80 per cent, but further progress is slow. Small bakers in particular are prone to neglect it.

Cereal enrichment had a strong bearing on the operation of this Fund and, incidentally, on my career. Even before the formation of the Food and Nutrition Board (Committee at first), I was invited in October, 1940 by Dr. Wilder to become chairman of its Committee on Cereals and to take a leading part in guiding the enrichment program. I accepted conditionally as outlined below.

A PERSONAL PROBLEM

This invitation appeared to furnish a providential opportunity for putting the product of my research to work for public benefit. At the same time it presented an important personal problem. I had reached an agreement for assignment of patents to Research Corporation which provided me with a share in the royalties. Therefore income from this would depend on the success of enrichment of flour and bread, at least in part. I was unwilling to accept a public appointment under such circumstances and subsequent events have amply justified my reluctance. I immediately worked out a revision of agreement such as would supply me with only a fixed and modest income of $15,000 a year and divert all the rest of my potential royalties, tax free, to a public cause on an irrevocable basis acceptable to the Bureau of Internal Revenue.

Legal stickling delayed for two years the formulation of such a revision and its formal acceptance by the Bureau.

In the meantime, I received the royalties, paid the tax on them, and devoted the residue to charities of my own choice. The permanent beneficiary of the revised arrangement was the American Friends Service Committee, Inc., which was chosen both because it is held in high public esteem and because it could not be held to be subject to my influence, since I had never been a member of the Society of Friends nor had I any past contact with the Committee or its work.

The Service Committee agreed that "the net proceeds from payments received by it hereunder will be used and applied by it to any or all of the charitable, philanthropic and relief purposes for which the Second

---

* R. M. Wilder and R. R. Williams. "Enrichment of Flour and Bread." *National Research Council Bulletin* 110. November, 1944.

Party (The Service Committee) is incorporated." Under this agreement, signed October 26, 1942, there has flowed directly from the coffers of Research Corporation into those of the American Friends Service Committee, Inc. the sum of $283,589.76 up to December 31, 1955. This statement is included here solely to stop the idle mouths of those who have accused me of profiteering.

THE NAME THIAMINE

A word may be in order here concerning the name thiamin or thiamine. When the synthetic product first came on the market it was not yet included in the annual publication, "New and Non-Official Remedies," of The Council on Chemistry and Pharmacy of the American Medical Association. And until so admitted, no product may be advertised in the pages of any reputable American medical journal. The Council at that time frowned upon the word "vitamin" as part of the name of any medicinal product. The word was regarded as implying a false and magical relation to life. Neither would the Council accept the name "aneurin"—which had been given to the substance by Jansen—because this word was held to imply a specific therapeutic utility.

Upon the specific request of the Council the writer proposed the name "thiamin" which was immediately accepted. The American Chemical Society's Committee on Nomenclature subsequently added an "e" for reasons of its own.

ENRICHMENT AND VITAMIN PRICES

It is also appropriate to discuss here the prices of the enrichment vitamins—especially thiamine—in relation to the cost of enrichment and especially in their bearing on the adoption of the practice in the early years.

It should be said at the outset that the price of thiamine has never been subject to the control of Research Corporation or of the Williams-Waterman Fund. Such control is forbidden by federal anti-monopoly legislation. The best that could be done was to insure that there were at least two licensed manufacturers and trust to competition to bring down the price.

At the beginning of flour and bread enrichment in May, 1941, the price of thiamine was the dominant factor in the cost. This was due not only to its rather high price at that time but also because riboflavin was then commercially unavailable and had to be omitted from the enrichment formula. In addition, the amount of niacin initially recommended, namely, 6 mgs. per pound of flour, was much too low to be effective. The standard was later raised to 16 mgs. per pound as the existing methods of analysis were improved and applied to major components of the American dietary.

Table I shows year by year the then prevailing prices of each enrichment ingredient. Often price changes were made by the manufacturers early or late in a given year. It has not appeared necessary or advisable to attempt to calculate a weighted price average for each year. Indeed, it would be impossible to do so with accuracy because it is general practice to make a price reduction retroactive to the extent of whatever inventory the customer may have on hand from his last previous purchase. The figures in Table I, therefore, merely indicate price trends in an approximate fashion.

TABLE I

Prices of Enriching Ingredients at Successive Dates

	Thiamine cents per gram	Riboflavin cents per gram	Niacin per Kilo	Iron (2) per Kilo	Total Nominal (1) Enrichment Costs per 100 lbs. Flour cents
January 1941	80				
May	65		$17.60	$1.54	12.3
January 1942	53			1.65	
April	48		14.30	1.65	9.0
July	41				
October	37				
May 1943	32		11.00	1.65	6.0
July	29				
October (3)	29	49	9.00	1.65	13.2
November	26.5	43			
January 1944	25	38	8.00	1.65	11.0
February	20	28	7.00	1.65	
August	18	23	7.00	1.65	
October	16	20	7.00	1.65	7.0
1945	16	20	7.00	1.54	6.9
1946	16	20	6.50	1.54	6.8
1947	16	15	6.00	1.54	6.2
May 1948	16	12.5	7.00	1.54	6.0
1949	16	12.5	8.00	1.65	6.2
1950	16	12.5	9.00	1.65	6.4
1951	16	12.5	9.00	1.26	6.4
December 1952	13.5	10	9.00	1.26	5.6
1953	13.5	10	9.00	1.21	5.6
1954	10	10	9.00	1.21	4.9
1955	8	8	8.00	1.32	3.9
1956	6	6	8.00	1.32	3.2

(1) This includes only the cost of the ingredients at minimum permitted levels, assuming zero levels of the nutrients in the flour to be enriched. Usually no deduction is made by the miller to compensate for natural content of the nutrients. The leading millers make a practice of adding a 10 per cent overage of the nutrients to overcome inaccuracies of distribution in the flour, also losses of thiamine during the few months storage of flour in warm, humid weather.

(2) The prices here are for reduced metallic iron, which is usually used in flour enrichment. For other forms of iron, such as pyrophosphate, which is white, the costs are somewhat higher.

(3) Riboflavin became available in quantity and was included in enrichment after this date. At the same time minimum niacin was raised from 6 to 16 mgs. per pound.

HOW ENRICHMENT STANDARDS WERE FIXED

A feature of early recommendations for enrichment standards which reflected our gross ignorance as of that time was the level of riboflavin to be used when it became available, namely, 1.2 mgs. per pound. Originally, this was supposed to be the level typical of whole wheat but subsequent experience showed that the method of analysis then in greatest use gave values for cereal products which were about twice as high as they should be.

This error was soon discovered. But the high recommendation was retained because evidence which had accumulated in the meantime strongly indicated that riboflavin deficiency was very marked where milk consumption was low—as in many parts of the South where deficiency disease was most prevalent. The Food and Drug Administration had, in the meantime, taken quite a definite position that evidence of need for a nutrient by significant segments of the population should control standards of enrichment. The theory of restoration to whole wheat levels which had dominated the earlier philosophy of enrichment for several participants was thus relegated to second place.

Another illustration of how a wise Providence, or perhaps dumb luck, steered us into favorable channels, involved the nutrient calcium. Prior to the introduction of formal broader scale enrichment there had been some sale, by Quaker Oats Company in particular, of farina to which vitamin D had been added. (Major legal battles resulted from this which we will not discuss here*). For this reason, primarily, vitamin D was permitted as an optional ingredient when formal standards were adopted. But, since vitamin D has largely to do with calcium metabolism, calcium was also made an optional ingredient. Neither optional ingredient has actually been used extensively.

CALCIUM IN ENRICHED FLOUR

An addition of calcium to flour had no appeal for the millers because the milling industry had been accused in previous decades of using plaster of Paris as an adulterant of flour. This adulteration, which at one time had actually been practiced at least occasionally, had long since ceased and the millers had no desire to reopen old wounds.

Our British cousins have often belabored us for not including calcium in our flour. Calcium is the one artificial ingredient which they do require in their "national wheat meal flour," an 80 per cent extraction product. They have a good reason for doing so: it counteracts the effect of phytin in the bran and germ retained in their flour—not in ours.

Americans have reached a practical solution through a fortunate circumstance, unfamiliar to most British scientists. The southern custom

---

* See reference, page 43.

of hot biscuits as the most popular form of bread long ago led to the production and sale in large volume of "self-rising" flour—that is, flour in which sodium bicarbonate and calcium acid phosphate are included as a leavening agent relieving the housewife of the need to use baking powder. This type of flour is peculiar to the United States. For self-rising flour 500 mgs. of calcium per pound is a required ingredient in enrichment. It just happens that in this country the hot biscuit areas are generally also the low milk areas. Milk is the other principal source of calcium in our food.

VITAMIN ASSAY METHODS

When enrichment was being introduced it is easy to appreciate that confusion as to analytical methods for the vitamins was worse confounded by the fact that such methods of analysis were being introduced for the first time and all at once into many scores of laboratories in the baking and milling trades.

Accordingly, one of the first undertakings in its own name of the Williams-Waterman Fund was a Vitamin Assay Conference in the Commodore Hotel, December 13, 1940. This involved a score of papers by workers of some experience and extended discussion by about 100 persons largely from the industries. Instruments as well as methods were critically evaluated and arrangements were made for the distribution to many laboratories of identical samples of bread and flour for comparative analyses by as many as could participate.

Concurrent and subsequent investigations by many of the participants were given later circulation within the group. Subsequent committee meetings also helped to resolve remaining difficulties and reasonably satisfactory methods were brought into general use in the course of a year or so.

In this as in many subsequent activities related to enrichment, I was not always sure whether I was acting for the Food and Nutrition Board as chairman of its Committee on Cereals or for the Fund. But it was often useful to have somebody to pay minor expenses, a duty which often was allotted to the Fund.

In general, it may be said that the Fund made no direct outlays to promote the adoption by millers and bakers of the practice of enrichment. Since the Fund's income was known to come from thiamine royalties, such action could have easily been construed as self-serving. We did not hesitate, however, to facilitate exchange of information about enrichment matters as in the above conference. Later we also contributed to the work of the Food and Nutrition Board but without designating for what purpose the money was to be employed or requiring any accounting.

In 1942-43, when corn meal enrichment was proposed, we agreed to promote vigorously the enrichment of whole corn meal by small Southern millers where a large element of education was required. This we have done on a large scale as recounted in Chapter V. We could do so because thiamine enters as an insignificant component of whole corn enrichment. The natural content of thiamine in whole corn is almost sufficient to meet standards.

PROFIT OR LOSS TO THE FUND FROM ENRICHMENT

I have often had occasion to consider how the income of the Fund was affected by the advent of cereal enrichment, just at the juncture at which thiamine became available in large quantities and at prices compatible with its use in a cheap staple consumed by everyone in substantial amounts. Many readers will be inclined to assume that this event came as a bonanza to the Fund. This assumption is, however, quite debatable.

Certainly, the total tonnage of thiamine produced and used was greatly enhanced by the adoption of enrichment. However, income to the Fund depends on price as well as tonnage. The rapid price reduction in the early years of synthetic thiamine surely would not have occurred had it continued to be used solely for medicinal purposes. In such a case a thiamine bulk price around 50 cents to $1 a gram might well have persisted for years. One is led to this belief by the prices of other vitamins which have not come into use for food fortification purposes. The present price of pyridoxine, for example, is 46 cents per gram; that of folic acid is $1.40 per gram.

The public has gained physiologically at the grocery store from enrichment; it has also gained, at least financially, at the drugstore.

On several occasions I've attempted to compute the amount of flour and bread which is being enriched in the United States from the amounts of the enrichment vitamins produced and sold in several recent years*. The arithmetical results have never been as satisfactory or convincing as one could wish. One difficulty has been ignorance of the carryover of stocks in hands of consumers from year to year; another has been that niacin and niacinamide have often been reported together in a single amount. (The amide is used exclusively for medicinal purposes; niacin is used both for foods and for medicines.) Still another uncertainty is introduced by the fact that much of the riboflavin used for enrichment of bread is supplied by milk incorporated in the dough.

In addition, figures on exports of vitamins have been lacking. About all one can say definitely is that thiamine production has exceeded the total required for the enrichment of all white flour and bread consumed

---

* U. S. Tariff Commission. "Synthetic Organic Chemicals. U. S. Production and Sales." (Published annually.)

in the United States by 80 to 150 per cent. Since we know that some unenriched white flour and white bread is sold, we must conclude that well over half the thiamine production is still used medicinally.

For example, in 1954 total production was 111,250 kilos; the total which would be required for enrichment of 200,000 cwt. of white flour would be 40,000 kilos. In the case of niacin, production has exceeded requirements for enrichment of flour and bread by 50 to 100 per cent or even more.

The U. S. Departments of Commerce and Agriculture jointly reported the use of synthetic vitamins and iron used in the enrichment of cereal products for both civilian and military use in 1948-50 as shown in Table II. These figures were obtained from responses to questionnaires from 22 or 23 firms engaged in (1) making flour premixes for their own mills; (2) selling premixes to flour mills; or (3) selling enrichment wafers to bakeries and restaurants.

There is also shown in Table II the production of each vitamin so far as published by the U. S. Tariff Commission for each of the three years.

TABLE II

Use for Cereal Enrichment vs. Production of Synthetic Vitamins in Kilos

	1948		1949		1950	
	Enrich-ment Use	Produc-tion	Enrich-ment Use	Produc-tion	Enrich-ment Use	Produc-tion
Niacin(1)	212,234	515,400	180,569	431,400	185,668	641,800
Thiamine	31,210	86,180	26,875	85,410	27,681	107,940
Riboflavin	16,539[3]	5,909	13,791	——(2)	14,129	——(2)

(1) Includes niacinamide. However, in earlier years when niacin and the amide were reported separately, the former exceeded the latter by 3 to 6 fold.

(2) Not reported.

(3) The riboflavin used for enrichment is largely derived from milk.

We prefer to let the reader form his own opinion as to whether enrichment has been financially profitable to the Fund. From the standpoint of the basic purpose of the Fund, to "combat dietary disease," it has been most profitable.

CHAPTER V

Dietary Reform
in the United States

In this vast country with its complex organization of food production, preservation, packaging, distribution and retail marketing, no major change in general dietary is possible without the expenditure of hundreds of millions of dollars. The provision of new food processing machinery necessary to introduce a new food product is only the initial step. New channels of distribution must be established. And moreover, if the product is to find a market, there must be large advertising expenditures. The moment some degree of success is achieved, competitive new products of greater or less merit arise and this threat to the infant industry is often severe.

These factors make it clear that the introduction of a new food product into general use is a major undertaking requiring substantial capital. Rarely can such an innovation be ascribed to a single firm or other agency. Yet, by the interplay of enterprise, such innovations frequently appear upon the scene. And each contributes something to the modification of prevailing food habits.

The progressive introduction of fruit juices and vegetable juices, especially tomato juice, as before-meal appetizers over the past two or three decades is a significant case in point, important from the standpoint of public health. Many new technological improvements—frozen foods, for instance—have contributed to the result. Still it would be difficult to apportion credit fairly for the essential dietary reform.

Other changes preceded these. Progressively increased use of refrigeration in the home, electrical or gas refrigeration gradually replacing the iceman, is a conspicuous example. Other innovations are now under way.

One which has been influenced by the work and opinion of the Food and Nutrition Board is the greatly increased retail distribution and use of skim milk. Another which has been almost entirely commercially motivated is the sale of ice cream-like frozen products embodying skim milk, butter or, in some cases, vegetable fats. Such developments do profoundly influence the dietary intake of nutrients over a period of years.

Few among these developments rely on claims of an essentially false nature; most of them embody sound nutritional principles as a reflection of the findings of nutritional science which illuminate our food industry.

MOTIVES OF MILLERS AND BAKERS

It was such an appreciation of nutritional science on the part of the millers and bakers of America which made a widespread and general adoption of the enrichment of white bread and flour possible. The firmness and persuasiveness of the bonds which join all leading millers in the Millers' National Federation, like factors uniting the members of the American Bakers Association, as well as the sound scientific leadership of the American Institute of Baking, alone made it possible to adopt the idea on an industry-wide basis.

In the early days of the program there was evidence that some millers and bakers were adopting enrichment in the hope of a competitive advantage over their fellows. In general this proved an illusory hope. Only as the millers and bakers came to appreciate that enrichment was for the advantage of the industry as a whole, rather than for any segment, did the program move forward into genuine effectiveness.

It is true, however, that this progress was greatly aided by the fact that State and City Nutrition Committees, Red Cross groups, schools and colleges, women's clubs and public utility dietitians began late in 1941 to teach the consumer to buy enriched bread and flour. By itself such teaching would have been quite insufficient to persuade the housewife to buy the enriched products at even a slight increase in price. It was, however, sufficient to convince the miller, baker and grocer that he would not lose trade by following the proposed pattern.

Two factors served to clinch the matter more than anything else; first, the bakers soon absorbed the cost of enrichment, selling enriched bread at the same price as unenriched and, second, the leading millers agreed to withdraw their unenriched brands of flour from the market.

Had it been necessary to overcome a slightly higher price by sheer education of the public, failure would have been reasonably certain. Or had it been necessary at the outset to prohibit by law the sale of the unenriched products, success would have been very doubtful. Such laws are well enforced only under exceptionally favorable circumstances.

ENDORSEMENT OF ENRICHMENT BY THE FOOD AND NUTRITION BOARD

Of course an endorsement by such a body as the Food and Nutrition Board was quite essential to success. The dissent of a minority of nutritionists from the decision caused considerable trouble during the earlier years—but for the most part, the motivation of the dissenters was not open to suspicion. They argued that the Board should have advocated the use of whole wheat flour and bread or something approximating them. Many thought that because the British eventually adopted such a measure with a great degree of success, we should do likewise. Had we been under constant threat of starvation by submarine blockade, as were the British, I believe the American people would have acquiesced. Short of that, however, such a measure would have been politically quite impossible. It would also have been extremely expensive since extensive protection of grain and mill products against insects and rancidity would have been necessitated by our climate, storage and milling conditions.

This true analysis of the situation is essential for consideration of the extension of cereal enrichment to other grains and other countries as discussed in this and succeeding chapters.

One other event needs to be mentioned, namely, that the fortification of oleomargarine with vitamin A has become almost universal in this country without agitation, propaganda or fanfare. The Food and Nutrition Board passed resolutions favoring it, the Food and Drug Administration permitted it, and industry progressively adopted it without further ado. It is most significant, however, that during this period oleomargarine was just breaking through the barriers, legal and otherwise, which had hampered its competition with the much more expensive butter. It would have been stupid, indeed, for the margarine manufacturers to neglect to repair the one conspicuous nutritional defect of their product when it could be done so cheaply.

Another fortification advocated by the Food and Nutrition Board and many others, namely the iodization of salt, has made relatively little progress in recent years, and only half of the country's table salt is now so treated. In this case there has been little commercial incentive to adopt the practice and no very effective trade association of salt manufacturers. The principal argument against it rules that it is difficult to distinguish at the point of origin between salt intended for human consumption and that destined for industrial uses. Apparently, relatively trivial factors may be sufficient to assure the success or defeat of a given food fortification program.

THE FUND ABSTAINS IN THE UNITED STATES

The Williams-Waterman Fund disclaims all substantial responsibility for the success of bread and flour enrichment in the United States. Its contributions to the cause have been quite minor: a conference on vitamin analysis in cereals, contributions to the general budget of the Food and Nutrition Board, and a few studies of the nutritive value of enriched bread by Dr. Westerman and her associates.

Corn Enrichment

Above: An old water mill.

Center: More typical crossroads mill.

Bottom: Dr. E. J. Lease at work on grits premix.

The Fund has made no direct outlays to promote the adoption by millers and bakers of the enrichment standards or the acceptance by the public of the enriched products. To have done so would have invited the criticism that we were seeking larger income through the sale of thiamine. Moreover, any measures we could have taken with money in hand would have had only a trivial effect.

THE FUND'S ADVOCACY ABROAD

We have been more active abroad in our support of flour and bread enrichment. Support of the survey of nutritional status at Norris Point, Newfoundland in 1944 and a resurvey there in 1948 by Dr. Grace Goldsmith and associates* had as its objective a determination of the value of cereal enrichment to such a population.

The results of these surveys tended to support the conclusion of other simultaneous and somewhat more extensive surveys by a larger group of doctors at the east coast outports of Newfoundland**, namely, that cereal enrichment markedly reduced the incidence of symptoms attributable to deficiencies of thiamine, riboflavin, niacin and iron while the incidence of other deficiency symptoms remained unchanged.

My lecture tours through the principal countries of Asia in 1950-51 and through Latin America in 1952 also emphasized cereal enrichment.

CORN MEAL ENRICHMENT

Enrichment of corn products in the United States has been the subject of one of the Fund's chief endeavors since 1942 and has involved a total expenditure of $203,000. The larger part of this endeavor has been exerted in and through Clemson Agricultural College, Clemson, South Carolina, where Dr. E. J. Lease has been a particularly effective leader. Dr. Lease has given elsewhere† a fairly comprehensive picture of the undertaking. We need only present a summary.

South Carolina in 1942 was the first state to enact legislation requiring that all white bread and flour sold within its boundaries shall be enriched. This pattern was later followed by 26 other states, as well as Puerto Rico and Hawaii. Concurrently, thought was given to the need for enriching corn meal, which, because of its low niacin content, had been associated with a high incidence of pellagra throughout the Deep South, especially during the first two decades of the present century. Both the high use of corn products and white flour were implicated. Low incomes, low availability of milk and lean meats, and the prevalent use

---

* *Journal of Nutrition 40,* 41 (1950).

** W. R. Aykroyd et al. "Medical Resurvey of Nutrition in Newfoundland 1948." *Canadian Medical Assn. Jour. 60,* 329 (1949).

† E. J. Lease. "Corn Meal Enrichment." *Jour. Amer. Diet. Assn. 29,* 866 (1953).

Corn Enrichment

Above: Successive designs of feeders.

Center: Premix ready to ship from Clemson.

Bottom: Display for county fair.

of fat pork and molasses all played a part in the prevalence of pellagra at that time.

The problem of enriching corn meal was complicated by the fact that at least half of the meal then consumed in the South was produced by little crossroads mills often operated by a single uneducated laborer. It was estimated that there were nearly 1,000 such mills in South Carolina alone and perhaps 8,000 in the entire South. Such mills produce whole corn meal and sometimes grits. Obviously, no enrichment legislation affecting these mills could be enforced without a prior substantial program of education both of millers and of housewives in the merits and purpose of enrichment.

Approximately half of the corn products used in the South are degerminated and come largely from bigger mills in the corn belt of the Middle West. The decision reached by South Carolina, and early copied by nearby states, was to require by law the enrichment of all degerminated corn meal brought in for sale. This was vigorously protested for a time as discriminatory by some of the millers but eventually all complied. In consequence, nearly all of the degerminated corn meal used throughout the South has been enriched for the past ten years.

While this battle between Southern state authorities and the Western corn millers was in progress, we began, under Dr. Lease's direction, our educational program among the small millers of South Carolina and their local customers. It was soon decided that a cheap automatic feeder must be designed to introduce the enrichment ingredients into the corn as it passed through the mill. Lease had the farm boy's practical, mechanical sense to do this.

Experimenting in the little mills with 8 or 10 successive designs, a model was finally chosen which could be made and sold for $25 on a no-profit basis and which was sufficiently rugged to stand up under years of use with a minimum of attention.

Thousands of these have been made in the Clemson shops using standard parts and cheap castings as far as possible. Hundreds of them have been shipped abroad for use in corn and rice enrichment projects. About 3,000 have been installed in Southern corn mills.

Lease also had to make a premix suitable for use in these feeders and had to devise a system for distributing it to millers and for collecting payment to cover the cost. No commercial premix manufacturer would undertake this as the bookkeeping charges on thousands of small accounts would have eaten up all possible profit. About 200 tons of such premix has been sold by Clemson throughout the South. All larger millers are encouraged to go to commercial suppliers.

THE AGRICULTURAL EXTENSION SERVICE

For the process of educating millers and housewives it has been necessary to rely on the Agricultural Extension Services, using County Agents to visit millers and Home Extension Agents to appeal to housewives. Only people such as these who already have the confidence of the farmers and their families can do such work effectively. Of course they have often been aided greatly by public health officers, women's groups, parent-teachers' associations and other civic-minded folks. State and local nutrition committees have often been of service in securing proper organization. Help has also come from the Home Economics Departments of the colleges.

Wherever the Agricultural Extension Service has been enlisted wholeheartedly the program has gone forward. At one time there was a hope that the Agricultural Extension Service in Washington could enlist the proper people throughout the South. Nonetheless, the doctrine of local autonomy is very strong and it has proved necessary to attack the matter state by state.

South Carolina was able in 1949 to amend its corn enrichment law to apply to whole corn as well as degerminated products. Alabama followed in 1953. In these two states very little corn meal of either variety now escapes enrichment. Whole corn meal enrichment is also carried on voluntarily in other states, notably North Carolina and Georgia. In general, the larger millers take the lead. We now believe that a third of the whole corn meal sold in the South is enriched.

CONTRIBUTION OF ENRICHMENT TO PUBLIC HEALTH IN AMERICA

A return of pellagra to the South seems wholly improbable as long as a reasonable degree of prosperity is maintained. Southern dietaries have greatly improved in many ways, due to greater industrial employment and the spread of dairying and diversified farming. If another great depression like that of the thirties should ensue, the maintenance of bread, flour and corn enrichment throughout the South would provide a mighty bulwark against nutritional disease. Being on a national basis, bread and flour and degerminated corn enrichment are extremely likely to endure even in a depression. Whole corn meal is more liable to neglect.

On the other hand, small corn mills are passing out of existence relatively rapidly as the improvement of roads and the availability of the automobile spread. The education which has been carried on in connection with enrichment will surely stand against endemic pellagra in the future of the South.

What cereal enrichment has accomplished elsewhere in the United States as a contribution to public health must be inferred from circumstantial evidence. The enrichment program was not undertaken as an experiment but as a reform measure, justified in the minds of its supporters by the then existing prevalence of deficiency diseases in recognizable forms.

Viewed as an experiment, it leaves much to be desired as no provision was made for a control element of population to be left unaffected by enrichment. Accompanying the introduction of enrichment, numerous changes in the national economy took place—many of them attributable to the war. Expansion of war industry occurred everywhere, but by no means evenly in extent or intensity. Large numbers of young men were withdrawn from civilian activity into military service. Many goods were rationed for civilian use because of the need to draw off large components of the country's productivity for military uses or for aid to our allies abroad. Indeed, the entire period when enrichment was being introduced was one of an economy more grossly disturbed than at any other time in our national history except perhaps during the Civil War. Hence, the effect of enrichment on public health was inescapably influenced by other important factors. For these reasons we cannot now nor in the foreseeable future draw irrefutable conclusions as to its benefits to public health.

We can, nevertheless, review those bits of evidence which seem to indicate an important benefit. First, the effect of enrichment in Newfoundland was precisely what would have been predicted, though here again some changes of the general economy ensued from the war conditions. But these were far less marked than in the United States.

The observable reduction in incidence of nutritional diseases in this country is great enough to convince one that something of importance has happened since 1940. All charity clinics, urban and rural, report a conspicuous drop in the incidence of symptoms of pellagra and beriberi. The leading medical schools specializing in nutrition now report it difficult to find cases of pellagra for purposes of instruction. Some of this may be due to betterment of dietaries in consequence of recovery from the previous depression and increased employment in war industry. Yet, as Dr. Jolliffe has pointed out, there has been no proportionate reduction in the incidence of mild scorbutic symptoms. This would point to cereal enrichment as an important causative factor.

Especially significant is the decline of pellagric symptoms among alcoholics, who, as a class, are in no condition to gain advantage from expanded opportunity for employment. We quote the following from Report 71 of The Medical Nutrition Laboratory of the Surgeon General of the United States Army by Figueroa et al:

"The only innovation since 1938 which bears on the alcoholic's nutriture has been vitamin enrichment of bread, started in Chicago in 1940-41. Alcoholic pellagra virtually disappeared from Cook County Hospital in 1942-43 when niacin, for flour enrichment, was first made by the ton. The alcoholic eats mainly fortified bread, and we conclude that this food habit has been the most significant factor contributing to the present surprising lack of avitaminosis among chronic alcoholics."

One should not suppose that the benefits of enrichment are confined to the derelicts of skid row or even to very low-income groups such as sharecroppers. Jeans, Smith and Stearns,** working with 404 pregnant women of low income in the relatively prosperous State of Iowa, have this to say: "The fact that the bread is enriched has certainly kept the majority of women of this study from deficiencies in iron, thiamine and riboflavin. The usefulness of the enrichment program is obvious."

We may never be able to state how large a segment of our population is benefited by enrichment. The opinion of Professor Henry C. Sherman* is as follows:

"It is reasonable to believe that the thiamine enrichment of breadstuffs has improved the health of a large proportion of the American people. But as there were no comprehensive statistics of the prevalence of subclinical neurasthenia, or of other forms of subclinical shortage of thiamine, we cannot expect to have any precise estimate of the influence of increased thiamine intake upon the number of people thus rescued from nerve and heart troubles, nor of the extent to which the more liberal amount of thiamine obtained through their food supply since 1940 has raised the general health level of the American people."

Corn products enrichment, as well as the inclusion of riboflavin, niacin and iron in the general enrichment formula, has certainly reinforced the benefits to which Professor Sherman alludes. We must be content with such general evidence and opinion. It furnishes us with good ground for the belief that we have witnessed the most abrupt and significant single reform of dietary habit which has occurred in recent generations. Its potential significance for the future and for the world at large will be discussed in a subsequent chapter.

---

* H. C. Sherman. *The Nutritional Improvement of Life*. Columbia Univ. Press, New York (1950), pp. 86-87.
** P. C. Jeans, Mary B. Smith and Genevieve Stearns. *Jour. Am. Diet. Assn.* 23, 27-34 (1952).

CHAPTER VI

Extension of Enrichment
to Other Continents

RICE ENRICHMENT IN ASIA

For several reasons application of the principle of enrichment of staple foods in Asia deserves special attention.

First, the eradication of beriberi was the chief objective visualized when the Fund was formed in 1935.

Second, Asia's hundreds of millions, constituting at least half of the human race, are grossly underfed and, in several densely populated areas, are subject to land pressure which must severely limit the successful application of agricultural betterments.

Third, Asia's vast illiteracy exposes her people peculiarly to the blandishments and shining promises of Communism.

Violent nationalistic reactions against former European colonial rule have started a vast conflagration which imperils the civilization of the entire world. At the bottom of it all is human misery, the want of adequate food and shelter for the masses. Perhaps in one or two more generations Africa will become the world's chief tinder-box. There are already abundant signs of this. In the present generation, Asia is the area of most acute peril. We can escape this in proportion to our success in filling empty bellies.

Rice is, of course, Asia's greatest food crop. It makes up 80 to 90 per cent of the caloric intake of a large majority of Asians. Hence, the nutritional shortcomings of rice present by far the largest single concrete food problem of human history to date.

The futility and ineffectiveness of the approach to this problem by both United States' and United Nations' agencies may yet prove to be the outstanding political blunder of the post-war period. We have a substantial remedy at hand, one capable of progressive betterment and expansion, but no major forces will adopt it because Western leaders do not understand the facts.

An effective job was done by FAO's Rice Commission in securing reasonably just distribution of the short supply of rice in the years immediately following World War II, but the nutritional faults of white rice have been ignored—except in several laborious conferences which adopted pious resolutions which everyone must have known would not be carried out.

UNDERMILLING OF RICE

Ever since about 1910, after Fraser and Stanton's demonstration that an exclusive diet of white rice will produce beriberi, the undermilling of rice has been preached unceasingly up and down the coasts of Asia. In Japan this teaching has had substantial effect due ultimately to both governmental edict and the greater feasibility of undermilling under Japanese conditions. Elsewhere in Asia it is doubtful that it has influenced the incidence of beriberi materially.

Japan has a much cooler climate than most of the rest of Asia. This limits the growth of weevils and the development of rancidity in undermilled rice, especially in winter months.

In the summer the technologically progressive Japanese fumigate all their brown rice in the mill warehouses. Even more important is the fact that all of Japan is electrified. Hence, rice mills are small and scattered throughout every neighborhood. Each mill serves its local community, and the housewife gets her rice fresh daily at the mill just as American housewives get their bread within 48 hours after it leaves the oven. Fresh milled rice is not at all unpalatable even though it retains a substantial amount of bran.

In north China, rice is commonly hulled or shelled at the farm, as it is in Japan, in order to reduce its bulk during shipment to the city market. The brown rice is milled in the cities such as Shanghai and Nanking. As the rice goes into the mill in north China in the summer months every handful of it contains scores of weevils which are crushed against the grains, their residues discarded with the bran.

Farther south in Asia shelling and milling (debranning) operations follow one another immediately at the mill, and rice is never shipped except either in the protective hulls or in the fully milled state. It would be impossible to send merchantable brown or undermilled rice from Rangoon, Bangkok or Saigon to north China or Japan without subjecting it to a deweeviling operation at its destination. The general Asian preference for white rice is due far more to dislike of weevils and rancidity than to mere prejudice as to flavor.

PARBOILING OF RICE IN INDIA

In India about 60 per cent of the rice crop is parboiled either at mills or, more often, in homes or in communally owned kettles in the villages, the operation being repeated in small batches once a week or so. Parboiling is an excellent protection against weevil attack. Small scale parboiling operations are feasible in India because of long dry seasons during which sun drying after parboiling is possible without danger of rain. The parboiling plants at mills simply shut down during the rainy season. Elsewhere in Southeast Asia the climate is not favorable to parboiling, and the practice is almost unknown except as it was introduced into Burma, Thailand and Malaya exclusively for the use of people of the Indian race.

In most of Indonesia, and in the hilly interiors of much of Southeast Asia, either domestic hand pounding or the use of small, primitive mills serving a local neighborhood prevail. Under these conditions undermilling is quite feasible because the rice is consumed within a few hours or days after milling. Much protection against beriberi is afforded by this practice, especially in Indonesia. It is, however, far less effective for the populations of cities, for personnel on rubber plantations, etc. who must get their rice from a distance. As opportunity for profitable industrial employment spreads to a community it becomes impossible to maintain these primitive practices since they consume hours of the housewife's day. Thus, rice grows whiter as urbanization and factory industry grow in Asia.

TRIALS OF RICE ENRICHMENT

By mid-1946 peace was sufficiently restored in Asia so that I could go there to explore the possibility of large-scale trials of enriched white rice. Attention was focused on north China and the Philippines as experimental areas. Plans were actually laid for a large-scale trial of rice enrichment in an industrial suburb of Shanghai in spite of many disadvantageous circumstances. Chief among these were Communist unrest, and the lack of geographical barriers to delimit the proposed experimental area and to direct the flow of rice to the area into well defined channels. Actually, little money was spent on this undertaking since it was very slow in getting under way because of lack of vigorous local leadership, and eventually it was rendered impossible by the advance of Communist armies.

The introduction of rice enrichment advanced much farther in the Philippines thanks to the excellent leadership of Dr. Juan Salcedo, Jr. with whom the subject had been repeatedly discussed in the United States in the dark days of 1942-43 when Dr. Salcedo's country was under Japanese control and when he was without news of his own family's fate. He returned to his native land in 1945 as a medical officer in General MacArthur's forces and was hard at work in the relief rehabilitation of his people when I arrived in August, 1946.

Rice Enrichment in Philippines

Above: Dr. Salcedo and staff of Institute of Nutrition, Manila.

Left: Analyzing enriched rice for vitamins.

Fortunately, his immediate family had survived the ordeal, but they and thousands of other once prosperous Filipino families had lost their homes through war's destruction and stood in dire straits for want of the bare necessities of life.

Snatching time from his urgent relief duties extending throughout the Islands, Dr. Salcedo entered enthusiastically upon the task of planning in detail the Bataan Experiment which has since become history. No more magnificent example can be cited of heroic forward-looking planning at a time when scores of thousands of Filipinos were sleeping on the ground under shelters made of packing cases or bits of galvanized roofing salvaged from their burnt homes. Food was entering Manila very irregularly, and thousands would have starved except for the U. S. Army rations doled out to long lines of civilians waiting at distribution centers.

THE BATAAN EXPERIMENT

Bataan, itself the scene of bitter fighting, was "scorched earth." Only by heroic measures were clinical teams organized to start a survey of the extent of beriberi in July, 1947. Some 12,384 people were examined, of whom 1,580, nearly 13 per cent, exhibited beriberi. There could be no doubt that Bataan was an endemic center of the disease, fairly typical of the Philippines as a whole.

In the meantime, a process for producing a rice premix protected from losses by washing* had been perfected on an adequate factory scale so it could be distributed in October, 1948 to all the rice mills of the east coast of Bataan. This, when mixed at the mill with white rice in the proportion of 1 to 200, would afford the same levels of thiamine, niacin and iron as in enriched flour in the United States.

The story of the Bataan Experiment has been told elsewhere** and will not be repeated here. Suffice it to say that a second clinical survey in 1949 revealed an extraordinary drop in the incidence of beriberi symptoms. Coincidentally, reported deaths from beriberi fell precipitously, and for seven months in 1950 no death from this disease occurred in the zone where rice had been enriched.

EXTENSION OF ENRICHMENT TO OTHER PROVINCES

At the conclusion of the Bataan Experiment in 1950 an attempt was made to extend rice enrichment on a self-supporting basis to nearby provinces producing large amounts of rice. The cost of rice enrichment during the experiment was subsidized for the 90,000 people involved, but this could not be extended to 700,000-800,000 people. Self-support meant an increase of slightly over 1% in the price of rice. Local laws soon were enacted against the sale of unenriched white rice. But they

---

* M. F. Furter et al. *Industrial and Engineering Chemistry, 38,* 486 (1946).
** "Better Health through Better Rice." Williams-Waterman Fund (1950).

were not enforced. Manila, a principal market for surplus rice, was not under such a law.

In August, 1952, a national law in the same sense was passed with bipartisan support. It was to become effective in successive provinces by presidential proclamation with reference to each. This measure provided time to teach the millers and to install the necessary mixing equipment. The national law was no better enforced, primarily because of opposition of the rice millers. If all obey the law there is no problem, but even a few violators can destroy enrichment by gaining the competitive advantage of a lower sales price for the unenriched product.

An additional and very severe handicap from 1950-1955 was the persistent refusal of the National Rice and Corn Corporation (NARIC), a government-financed agency, to provide for the distribution of the rice premix to accessible points where millers could readily buy it. NARIC manufactured the premix satisfactorily and delivered it to its warehouses in provincial capitals, but would go no further.

Two trips to the Philippines in late 1953 and early 1954 resulted in a plan to transfer premix manufacture and distribution to a private company financed and managed by Arturo Tanco, a chemical engineer with much experience in the rice trade. Others were, of course, free to enter into competition with him.

After months of argument with NARIC and a few others, this plan was adopted in January, 1955. We had the aid of 22 scientific and civic organizations which joined in a memorial to President Magsaysay urging implementation of the rice enrichment law and the adoption of a schedule which would bring the entire Philippines under the law by the end of 1956.

OPPOSITION TO RICE ENRICHMENT

We also had the opposition, apart from NARIC, of Amando Dalisay, Harvard Ph.D. in economics and a pupil of John Black. His argument was that the Philippines cannot afford the annual import of $1,300,000 worth of vitamins, even though the islands have been importing for many years 50 to 100 million dollars worth of processed and canned foods annually. He has been influenced by Eric Huzenlaub, inventor of the Rice Conversion Process, who has been in Manila for the past five years.

Of course, rice conversion would serve to eradicate beriberi if a way could be found to introduce it. Because of climate, fuel drying would have to replace sun drying, as used in India. This would necessitate a few large rice conversion plants since fuel drying is infeasible on a small scale. Hence, 10 or 20 large mills would have to replace the present 8,000 small mills with a capital investment of 100 to 200 million dollars. There would be infinite problems of indemnifying the present small mill owners for their losses. Huzenlaub has meager capital and can arouse no enthusiasm for rice conversion as the Filipino people have shown a strong dislike for converted rice. Of course there is no obstacle in law or otherwise to the introduction of rice conversion in parallel with rice enrichment. A single site where it could be tried could easily be found if capital of a few hundred thousand dollars were available.

During the first eight months of 1955 rice enrichment advanced rapidly, total production exceeding all previous years combined. Competition in premix production under a process devised by Merck & Co. Inc. began in August and September. The first effect of this was disturbing, since the new competitor, a wealthy Chinese, directed his efforts to areas where Tanco had already worked rather than new areas where the law was just going into effect. It is hoped that an understanding will be reached which recognizes that every area must be cultivated even where rice production is meager and the sale of premix unprofitable.

More recently there has been disturbing political activity on the part of rice millers' organizations with the aid of a leading politician seeking the repeal of the enrichment law and even the abolition of the Institute of Nutrition. At times this has seemed a serious threat, but Secretary of Health Garcia and Dr. Salcedo have retained the support of President Magsaysay. No doubt the enforcement of the law is a burden to the government and unless nearly 100 per cent enforcement can be achieved, the law tends to penalize the law-abiding miller by putting him in competition with violators who have the advantage of a one per cent lower cost. Only Filipino public opinion can determine the outcome.

At present the law is nearly completely enforced in Manila where Dr. Icasiano, the Director of Health, is unreservedly for the program. In the Provinces where the need is greater because of higher incidence of beriberi, enforcement is effective with respect to only 5 to 10 per cent of the output. Effort is being made to secure support of rice millers' organizations by offering them aid in their problems of taxes on milling operations.

In the interest of completeness, reference must be made to a publication by FAO entitled "Rice Enrichment in the Philippines".* A critique of this report has been published which points out its failure to evaluate the evidence objectively.** Fortunately, the weaknesses of the report are so obvious that it has never been cited by opponents of enrichment in the Philippines so far as I am aware.

RICE ENRICHMENT PROSPECTS ELSEWHERE IN ASIA

A tour throughout the principal rice-eating countries of Asia, apart

---

* F.A.O. Nutritional Studies No. 12. March, 1954.
** "Food Fortification in the Orient." *Nutrition Reviews 12,* 289 (1954).

Rice Enrichment in Philippines

Above: Checking enrichment of rice intercepted in transport.

Right: Dr. Helen Burch analyzing blood specimens.

from China and Korea, then inaccessible because of war, was made in 1950-1951. In brief, the prospect of the early, effective adoption of rice enrichment in these countries is not bright for several reasons.

1—Excepting in the Philippines and Japan there are no statistics on mortality from beriberi, and there is little awareness of this disease as a major problem.

2—Governments, accordingly, have no resolute intention of action in the matter.

3—Import of vitamins on a large scale is unlikely as shortage of dollars dictates severe restrictions on all imports from abroad.

In India, the beriberi problem is greatly mitigated by the widespread use of parboiled rice. In the Telegu area of Andhra State, where white rice is strongly preferred by the masses, an attempt was made to set up a clinical survey of beriberi under the state health department but negligible progress has been made during five years' time in spite of subsidy by this Fund.

In Burma, white rice is strongly preferred and there must be great need for correcting its shortcomings, though statistics on beriberi are lacking. The fact that rice is customarily cooked in an excess of water which is discarded makes rice enrichment much less attractive.

In Thailand, the Thai Rice Co. has been operating a rice premix plant for about six years. Sales of the product are, however, very small. There is considerable beriberi in North Thailand; severe outbreaks have been reported repeatedly in the Chiengmai area in recent years. Yet the government is little conscious of the problems, and certain persons in the FAO Regional Office there still entertain visionary ideas of introducing some form of parboiling. Accordingly, nothing is being attempted for the masses.

In Malaya, a premix plant has operated in Singapore for several years but in a casual, opportunist fashion as in Thailand.

In South Vietnam and adjacent territories, formerly under French control or influence, there is a large production of white rice. Saigon was once the largest rice exporting port of Asia but has lost rank as compared with Bangkok and Rangoon. War and unrest through many years have made practical progress in rice enrichment impossible.

In Indonesia, rice production and milling, while quite extensive, are primitive in organization. Industrialization, apart from agricultural industry, is quite slight. Each of the numerous small mills provides a limited area with undermilled rice, thus reducing the extent of beriberi. Governmental control of the degree of milling is nominal, no formal standards having been framed. The large cities and some plantations are supplied with imported white rice during periods after local supply is exhausted. This imported white rice should be enriched, but the government is considerably preoccupied with scores of other urgent problems.

Thailand, Malaya and Indonesia are not short of dollars to the extent that other Asian countries are. Exports of rubber, teak, tin and rice provide fairly liberal foreign exchange.

Reference has been made on page 38 to the trials of enrichment in Formosa.

In Japan, an indigenous endeavor to promote rice enrichment is now under way. Four leading pharmaceutical firms are making premix, utilizing thiamine of Japanese manufacture. No indication has arisen of government intention to introduce compulsory enrichment. Government supervised undermilling has worked fairly well in spite of a popular preference for white rice. Japanese competition in supplying vitamins to enrich the rice of the rest of Asia must be anticipated in the future.

CEREAL ENRICHMENT IN LATIN AMERICA

The introduction of cereal enrichment in Latin America is in general handicapped by the same factors mentioned with reference to Asia, namely, the want of data on incidence of deficiency disease, indifference of governments to public health problems, unless they are politically weighted, and shortage of dollars with which to buy vitamins.

In addition to these, there are many complexities arising from the fact that the staple cereal is sometimes wheat, sometimes rice, sometimes corn or even some other starchy product such as cassava. In some areas all these products are found side by side in the markets, each preferred by some element of population. In general, Latin Americans do not use cereals in the same high proportions as do rice-eating Asians. Nevertheless, the total consumption of refined cereals, i.e., white flour, white rice and cassava plus the consumption of corn, short in niacin, is such as to afford tremendous nutritional advantage from appropriate enrichment if that were possible.

The gain to the masses would be vastly greater than that which has been obtained in the United States but presumably less than could be achieved in rice-eating Asia. We shall not speak of wheat-eating Asia as we have made no special study of those areas.

The Indian populations of Central America and of the Pacific and Andean areas largely use corn as their staple grain. Corn is, however, produced mainly in little patches and processed to edible form in the home. There is a minimal industrial production of corn, hence factory type enrichment does not apply. Home enrichment is out of the question. If sufficient dissemination of knowledge were achieved in homes it would be simpler for the people to take pills or protective foods.

I have already mentioned the relative absence of pellagra in Guatemala and Mexico. Until we understand that situation we can not advise these people on their grain supply. A limited factory production of tortilla flour is occurring on the outskirts of Mexico City and this is being enriched. Perhaps there will be a great extension of this practice for the benefit of city dwellers in the future.

White flour in the form of bread and white rice as the boiled grain are commonly used by Spanish-speaking Latin Americans, who for the most part have considerable Spanish blood. In general, white bread is used more widely than white rice. In Chile and in Northern Brazil little rice is consumed. In the lowlands of Colombia and of Ecuador and in the southern part of Sao Paulo, Brazil, rice outranks white bread in importance.

The statistics of production versus import of both of these products are extremely variable from country to country. Ecuador and Honduras, for example, produce a surplus of rice; all other Latin American countries import at least a portion of their supply. Most Latin American countries produce some wheat, sometimes at fabulous costs—as in upland Colombia. Some additional supply is imported, partly as wheat to be milled locally, partly as flour for immediate sale to homes and bakeries.

On account of these complexities, proposed cereal enrichment laws must take account of enforcement both in local mills and at ports of entry. Often there are also conflicts of interest between local producers and importers. As we have seen in the Philippines, there are problems enough to deal with even when only a single cereal is involved and when it is all of domestic origin. One can imagine the difficulties when both rice and wheat are involved and when part of each is imported, some in rough form, some in finished form—as is so often the case in the Latin American scene.

For Latin America it is simpler to enrich flour than rice. No protection against washing loss being involved, the enrichment of flour is cheaper to begin with. And since all North American millers enrich their flour, the Latin American buyer can always get it simply by asking for it wherever flour importation is economically in order.

By contrast, North American rice millers have been persistently reluctant to enrich thus far. The Latin American buyer must demand enriched rice and must be prepared to meet all manner of excuses and protestations against enrichment on the part of North American suppliers. A genuine popular demand for enriched rice in Latin America will ultimately break this resistance down, but at present the Latin American buyer must have strong convictions and be prepared to fight for them. Few such convictions have as yet developed in Latin America, and people who hold them are not usually in the saddle.

PUERTO RICO'S SUCCESS
Puerto Rico had such convictions induced by the work of Dr. Lydia

Latin America

Above: With Dr. Philip White and Mr. Nicolini, leading miller of Lima, Peru.

Center: The author and wife in the highlands of South America.

Chilean Leaders

Right: Seated: Drs. Jorge Mardones, Natividad Segovia de Riquelme, Hermann Niemeyer. Standing: Drs. Riquelme and Santa Maria.

Enrichment, Cuba

Above: Sampling enriched rice in Havana with Dr. Cosme de la Torriente and Mrs. Louise F. Smith.

Below: Medical advisory committee of Fundacion de Investigaciones Medicas.

Roberts. Puerto Rico also has a strong, shrewd and civic-minded governor in the person of Luis Muñoz Marin. On his insistence the Puerto Rican legislature adopted compulsory rice fortification in May, 1951. Many United States rice millers protested vehemently, and their constitutional lawyers freely predicted the early downfall of Western civilization. Puerto Rico quietly went ahead and enforced the law without the slightest difficulty.

All Puerto Ricans have been getting enriched rice for the past five years. The result was accomplished so quietly that most Puerto Ricans are not even aware that their health is now protected by a different form of rice than they used to get. However, it should be noted that Puerto Rico's problem was quite simple because it imports all the rice it uses.

Furthermore, all the rice they get passes in interstate commerce and is subject to the jurisdiction of the United States Food and Drug Administration. Falsely labeled rice is subject to seizure en route. Hence all Puerto Rico has to do is to inspect in routine fashion at the ports of entry.

CUBA

Our Fund has done far more work in Cuba in behalf of rice enrichment than in all other Latin American countries combined. Great efforts have been made during the last eight years by the *Fundacion de Investigaciones Medicas,* Havana, to educate the people to demand enriched rice. Much of this educational endeavor has been futile because it has not been possible to maintain even token quantities of enriched rice continuously on the Cuban market. One cannot effectively teach people to buy and use a given product unless they can buy it in a nearby market.

Compulsory enrichment laws for flour and rice have been framed and even passed by the legislative body, but they have died without presidential signature. There can be no doubt that this is due to active opposition by large elements of the rice and flour trades.

No Cuban champion of sufficient political influence has yet come to the support of these needed health measures. Cubans eat on an average 80 pounds of white flour and 120 pounds of white rice per annum. With so much refined cereal in the Cuban diet enrichment is imperative!

CHILE'S FLOUR ENRICHMENT PROGRAM

In view of the current situation there is no immediate prospect of general rice enrichment in any Latin American country. But in respect to white flour the prospect is much better. Chile long since took the lead in this under the guidance of Chilean statesmen and public health workers. Eduardo Cruz-Coke, Jorge Mardones, Julio Santa Maria, Alfredo Riquelme and Carlos Campbell del Campo deserve especial mention.

[73]

Campbell has been the active and practical leader in introducing flour enrichment in substantially all Chilean flour mills. It took effect January 1, 1954 and, according to latest information, is proceeding quite successfully—this in spite of dollar shortage problems under which Chile suffers.

The people of Chile eat very little rice indeed. If they consumed as much as most Latin Americans, we should doubtless have long since experienced effective aid in rice enrichment from the strong group of Chileans mentioned earlier.

Enrichment of imported white flour is required by law in Guatemala and San Salvador. Some enrichment of flour is practiced in Lima, Peru, and there has long been persistent discussion both in Peru and in Colombia of countrywide enrichment. The difficulties in these countries of dollar shortage, of geographical variation in dietaries, and in population types from one region to another are considerable. In Venezuela, all flour is imported from the United States. There is no dollar shortage, and the government has lush reserves of oil royalties. Flour and rice enrichment have both been discussed for three or four years. The authorities seem paralyzed only by the long habit of inaction.

In Brazil, the State of Sao Paulo has long been eager for flour enrichment and has an interest in rice as well. Dollar shortage problems and want of sympathy on the part of the National Government at Rio de Janeiro have long delayed effective decision.

The idea of enrichment of both these cereals has been planted widely throughout Latin America and may grow to major proportions in future years.

FOOD ENRICHMENT IN EUROPE

European attitudes toward food fortifications differ sharply from one country to another. As far as I have been able to learn, France, Spain, Portugal and Italy have been little concerned with such possibilities as measures for application to their general populations.

In France, food enrichment is substantially prohibited by the restriction of the sale of fortified foods to pharmacies. Indeed, with predominantly French leadership, there is now running through continental Europe, apart from Scandinavia, a wave of protest against the addition of any sort of chemical substance to foods regardless of purpose. This movement appears to have its origin in strictly academic circles among professors who have only fragmentary knowledge of modern food technology or its problems. Much of the propaganda being issued reflects an ill-informed opinion that the only possible motive for chemical additives is debasement of the food supply with fraudulent intent. Much of it might well have been composed by school boys in remotest Africa desirous of producing essays which will earn their teachers' commendation.

Switzerland, Holland, Belgium, Italy and some others permit the addition of vitamins to foods at levels approved by the government. Claims for beneficial effect must have prior approval of local health authorities. Actual practice of food fortification under these circumstances is negligible except perhaps as a token of further future reconsideration.

SCANDINAVIA

The Scandinavian countries have welcomed the food fortification principle more affirmatively. Denmark leads in this, requiring fortification of all white flour in a manner resembling that prevailing in the United States. Niacin is not required, but calcium is. Riboflavin levels are about twice as high as ours. Denmark also requires the fortification of margarine with 20 international units of vitamin A and 0.5 international unit of vitamin D per gram, levels similar to our own.

In Sweden, neither flour nor margarine fortification is compelled by law. However, it is followed voluntarily in the major part of the production of flour and of substantially all the margarine. Both A and D are added to margarine.

Norway requires a similar fortification of margarine but flour enrichment is little practiced.

Germany has no compulsory food fortification. Most margarine is fortified, but only negligible amounts of flour are enriched. The sale of vitaminized foods is permitted by regulations dating from 1942, but the practice is limited except in the case of margarine.

BRITISH POLICY

Great Britain has been the scene of extensive debate of the principle of food fortification. As early as July 1940* the British government decided to fortify all flour and bread with thiamine, but never actually carried it out.

Because of war conditions British thiamine production was delayed and has not since risen to very substantial levels. Incidents in Parliament gave rise to the suspicion that vitamin manufacturers were destined to reap inordinate profits. Nutritional leaders came to favor in preference undermilling of flour, a practice disliked by the millers and therefore unsuccessful until it was made compulsory in April, 1943. The addition of 7 ounces of calcium carbonate per 280 lb. sack of 80 to 85 per cent extraction flour was required. The production and use of this type of flour is still maintained by government subsidy.

However, since August, 1953, whiter flours have been permitted. But for such flours an addition of 1.65 milligrams of iron, 0.24 milligrams of

---

* T. Moran and J. C. Drummond, *Nature 146,* 117 (1940).

vitamin B$_1$ and 1.60 milligrams of nicotinic acid per 100 grams of flour, as well as 14 oz. of calcium carbonate per 280 lb. sack, is required by law. Such flours do not enjoy government subsidy, and sell at a higher price and therefore in minor volume as compared with the long extraction "National Flour." Since 1954, fortification of all margarine with vitamins A and D is also required.

The early decision of British food authorities to turn to long extraction flour seems to us to have been well justified by the threatened submarine blockade. They needed to maintain substantial food stocks in their Island Fortress, and the needed cereal could be shipped and stored more economically as grain. They needed grist for the existing British mills to aid in conserving their foreign exchange. They needed the mill by-products as cattle feed. Furthermore, their people, with their backs to the wall, could be persuaded to lay aside their preference for white flour as a means to save their country. The continuation of this policy in the post-war period may also have been justifiable as an economic measure to conserve their foreign exchange.

BRITAIN'S ATTITUDE TOWARD ENRICHMENT ELSEWHERE

I have not, however, viewed with sympathy the disposition of many British nutritionists, under the leadership of the British Medical Research Council, to call upon the rest of the world to follow their example in this matter. We shall see presently how ineffective this policy was in Canada—in spite of a very high loyalty to the British Crown.

Indeed, my own observation is that peoples who have adopted highly refined cereals can rarely—if ever—be persuaded to revert to retention of the bran. There are often sound economic reasons against it, as in the case of rice in Asia. Apart from this, it requires a very hardy and trusting soul to undertake to change the long established preferences of a people with regard to their chief staple food. It seems to me well nigh impossible.

There appears to exist among many British nutritionists a prejudice against the addition of artificial substances to foods. The reason for this prejudice is somewhat difficult to discern, but it seems to arise primarily from a mistrust of private industry. It appears to be an expression of a socialistic doctrine, "if anyone makes a profit out of anything it must be wrong, no matter how beneficent to others." I shall not attempt to argue the merits of socialism versus private enterprise. I can only express faith that the facts as outlined above will presently be generally recognized. (See Addendum, August 1, 1956, page 77.)

CANADIAN ENRICHMENT

We conclude this chapter with an account of flour enrichment in

Canada. Although from the beginning of the enrichment program in the United States, Canadian millers desired to follow the same pattern, the Canadian government adopted obstructive tactics. In 1942 "Canada Approved" flour and bread were adopted on a voluntary basis following the British long-extraction principle. They never came into use sufficiently to have a practical nutritional effect. Through many years—until 1953—Canadian law pharisaically declared any addition of vitamins to flour or bread "an adulteration." The result was a stalemate. It was politically impossible to make "Canada Approved" flour and bread compulsory.

When Newfoundland became Canada's tenth province in 1949, Newfoundland insisted on retaining its compulsory enrichment program, first adopted in 1944. This fact perhaps had influence upon Canadian thinking for in February, 1953 a voluntary program of enrichment of white flour and bread, very similar to that of the United States, came into effect in all provinces of Canada, except Newfoundland, where it remains compulsory.

The Bakery Foods Foundation of Canada says, under date of February, 1955, "It is estimated that up to 90 per cent of all commercially made white bread in Canada is now enriched." I am unable to defend the accuracy of this estimate, but all observers agree that the practice is widespread and general. I am sufficiently simple-minded to regard the question, "Does it work?" as an all-important test of value.

For the benefit of our sincerely socialistic British cousins it can be said without fear of successful contradiction that the milling and baking industries of North America have made no measurable profits from enrichment. They have perhaps retarded somewhat the slow and steady decline in consumption of cereal products versus other more expensive foods such as milk, meat, eggs, etc. It is impossible to measure this benefit, if any, which has been more or less evenly distributed throughout the two industries.

The vitamin manufacturers have, of course, made large profits, but, as discussed in Chapter IV, it is impossible to say whether these profits have been less or greater because of enrichment. The larger profits are still derived from medicinal vitamin preparations. Under a free economy no one can force upon the public his views as to how much or how little it should spend for these products. I freely disclaim omnipotence.

Addendum, August 1, 1956.

As we go to press, we have just had opportunity to read "Report of the Panel on Composition and Nutritive Value of Flour" presented to Parliament May 1956. London, H. M. Stationery Office Cmd. 9757. This Henry Cohen report is most gratifying to American supporters of flour and bread enrichment as it reflects many of the views which have heavily influenced our thinking for the past 15 years or more. We understand that the subsidy for long extraction flour will terminate September 29, 1956.

CHAPTER VII

Kwashiorkor
and the Future

Deficiency diseases due to lack of one or more vitamins or mineral elements still occur in every country of the world*. Even in the most prosperous and best informed countries of the West statistics of the occurrence and severity of these diseases are far too meager. In Asia, Africa, South and Central America and their nearby islands, information is merely fragmentary. Often all that is known is the frequency with which these diseases are reported in hospitals. Most of the world's populations avoid hospitals as they avoid undertakers, hence hospital admissions constitute no fair sample of the people. Besides, few of the available doctors would recognize most of the deficiency diseases unless full blown and classical in type.

Perhaps one of the greatest future tasks of this Fund may be to conduct clinical surveys of nutritional status in as many lands as possible. Experience is improving our methods, the costs are not prohibitive, and the information would be invaluable.

All of the deficiency diseases mentioned above would quickly yield to proper enrichment programs. In some instances it may be even easier and cheaper to attack them by better distributed use of foods already at hand. The use of fruits to counteract and prevent scurvy, and yellow vegetables to offset vitamin A deficiency, are among the more feasible examples. However, don't forget that you can supply all the vitamins a person needs for 10 years at far less cost than you can re-educate him in food habits—disregarding for the moment other merits of education.

PROTEIN MALNUTRITION

We come now to consider protein malnutrition for which no remedy is immediately available either via enrichment or by the far more laborious, costlier and slower processes of agricultural reform.

* American Geographical Society of New York, "Study in Human Starvation, Diets and Deficiency Diseases." 1953.

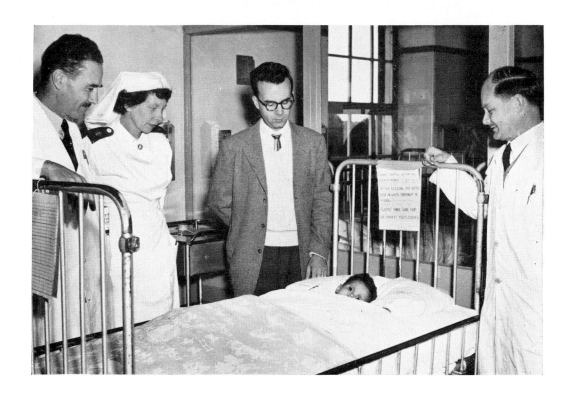

Kwashiorkor

Above: Drs. John F. Brock, H. E. Schendel and John D. L. Hansen around a tiny patient's bed.

Right: Dr. Nevin S. Scrimshaw, in Central America, is concerned with all dietary diseases, including kwashiorkor.

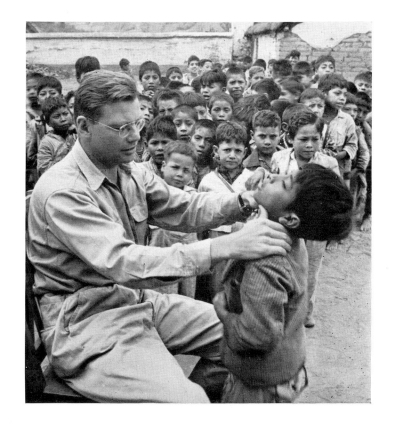

By far the most prevalent form of protein malnutrition is that known by its African name, kwashiorkor. This is a severe and often fatal disease of weaned children, usually within the age range of 2 to 5 years. It is undoubtedly brought on by the transition from feeding at the mother's breast to subsistence on whatever other food is readily available, often predominantly a gruel of one of the cereals. The commonest symptoms are loss of appetite, diarrhea, edema which may be localized in legs and feet, hyperpigmentation and dryness or wrinkling of the skin, followed in later stages by exfoliation and ulceration of the skin which may cover half the area of the body.

A very distinctive sign in black-haired races is bleaching of the hair to a sandy red. This may occur in sharp bands reflecting successive improvements and worsenings of the nutritional status. The hair is also often thin and can be pulled out at its roots without pain. Biochemically, blood serum albumin is low, often very low, while the globulin remains normal or even rises. Moderate anemia is usual. At autopsy the liver is often enlarged but not always; it is more commonly fatty. The pancreas has often been reported fibrotic.

The precise cause of this disease is far from clear for it occurs among peoples whose predominant cereal is corn—as in Guatemala or South Africa, or white wheat flour—as in Chile, or rice—as in Indonesia, or millet—as in parts of India.

It is known where mixtures of one or more of these carbohydrate foods are eaten often in conjunction with bananas, taro or cassava. There is general agreement that the total protein intake of children which succumb to this disease is low, that the proteins present, being of vegetable sources, are of relatively poor biological value. There is also a good measure of agreement that the most effective treatment of kwashiorkor is a diet containing fairly abundant animal protein. Therapeutic experience therefore broadly confirms analyses of the provocative diets.

The disease has been studied by scores of groups throughout the world. Much of this endeavor has been aimed at better definition of the disease, at better diagnosis and at practical combinations of locally available foods which may be useful in treatment or in prevention. Major effort has been made to meet the economic factor which underlies this worldwide disease. The question as to what combinations of available foods will be effective and yet be cheap enough for the pocketbooks of the parents has often dominated humanitarian interest.

THE ETIOLOGY OF KWASHIORKOR

Little attention has been paid to the determination of the cause of the disease in chemical terms. The history of scurvy, beriberi and pellagra clearly shows how success in prevention and treatment awaited the chemical identification of the missing substance. It is reasonable to suppose that the same will prove true of kwashiorkor. Certainly if we knew that kwashiorkor were due to a lack of substance X, we could analyze the foods of all the world for X and prescribe the best available diets wherever the disease occurs.

Such a simplified view of the matter does not appeal to the majority of physicians. They are too impressed with variability of symptoms. Earlier workers on the classical deficiency diseases suffered from the same confusion because beriberi, pellagra and scurvy often occur in association with one another or with ariboflavinosis.

The chemical approach requires focusing on the precise compositional differences which distinguish the diets which cure the disease from those that cause it. To assume in advance, without evidence to that effect, that the disease is caused by a lack of a combination of two or more things is in effect to consign the solution of the problem to a future generation. Moreover, there is no past precedent for this in the history of nutritional disease.

PROFESSOR BROCK'S PROJECT

We were accordingly delighted to discover that Professor John F. Brock of Cape Town, a man of wide experience with kwashiorkor and highly esteemed in international circles, also shared these views and was eager to undertake research with a determination of chemical etiology as his prime objective.

He recognized, as do we, that the problem is a very difficult one, primarily because there is no experimental animal in which indisputable kwashiorkor can be developed. Hence, the work must be done with human subjects, in areas where the disease occurs abundantly. And it must be done without avoidable sacrifice of human life. This is no small handicap as compared with the availability of suitable experimental animals in the case of all the classical deficiency diseases which have so far been attacked successfully. It is no worse, however, than pernicious anemia which has already yielded to a chemical approach.

Professor Brock and his associates have indeed had remarkable success so far. Beginning with the fact that skim milk is curative, he next showed that casein in various states of purification also cures. Proceeding from this to amino acid mixtures*, he has again succeeded in initiating cures, ultimately with only 11 amino acids** of which 8 are Rose's essential ones.

---

* Brock, Hansen, Howe, Davel, Pretorius and Hendrickse. "Kwashiorkor and Protein Malnutrition." *Lancet,* Aug. 20, 1955, p. 355.

** Brock, Hansen and Howe, *Amer. Jour. Clinical Nutrition 4,* 286 (1956).

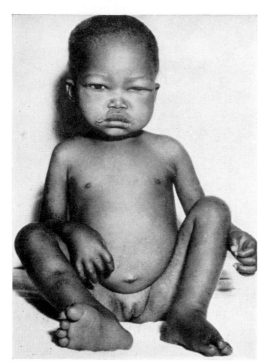

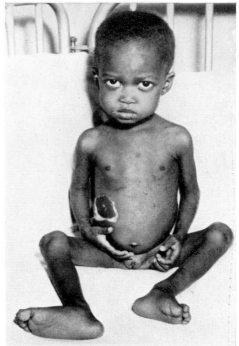

South African kwashiorkor baby's response to amino acids. *Left:* upon admission. *At Right:* Edema dissipated in 14 days. The child's stupor gone, the infant was soon restored to vigorous health. J. F. Brock.

Bottom Right: Edema and dermatitis of kwashiorkor, Patwardhan, India.

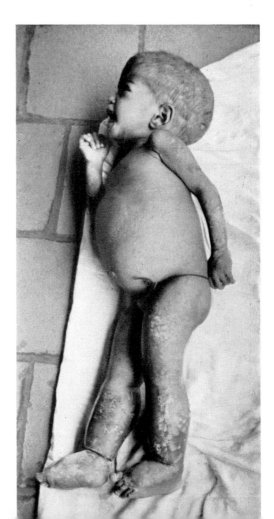

The further prosecution of the problem now would be easy if the experimental animal could be used. Further simplification of the formula must be approached gingerly lest the successful experiment, which reveals what cannot be omitted, endanger the life of the child. Perhaps, by some supplementary approach, clues can be had which will facilitate the final and crucial experiment. At all events it does not seem unreasonable to hope that within two or three years Professor Brock will be able to announce the curative substance.

THE FUTURE ATTACK ON KWASHIORKOR

When this is done, measures must be taken to employ this knowledge for a world-wide attack upon the most formidable nutritional disease which now presents itself. The needed substance, from present indications, may very well turn out to be one of the essential amino acids. Beyond doubt, all 8 essential ones will be required to achieve normal nutrition over any extended period. In certain instances we already have animal evidence that a proper balance between one amino acid and another will have to be observed. All essential nutrients, including vitamins, minerals and amino acids, must somehow be supplied for growing children. Hence, the task will be intricate.

It will also be economically difficult because the best sources of all essential amino acids are animal foods, expensive foods, which much of the human race cannot now afford. The approach to this problem via synthetic chemistry may be more difficult economically than an attack on beriberi or pellagra by one or two orders of magnitude. Vitamins are required daily by the human being in quantities of micrograms or milligrams. The amino acids are needed in decigrams or grams. Hence, the wanting amino acid must be made at a cost of the order of $1 a pound. If it costs $10 or more, we might as well order a nice beefsteak and a quart of milk a day for each member of the human race, knowing full well that it will never be delivered.

The great significance of the food fortification which we have seen launched in the United States is to show that the efforts of the farmer can be supplemented effectively by those of the chemist. The farmer must continue through future centuries to produce the carbohydrates, fats and proteins which constitute a large proportion of human food needs. There is, however, no basic reason why we should not call on the chemist to make all the minor but essential components which he can produce competitively.

What he can do for a dollar or a shilling will not be known until we give him a clear road to the potential market. We have seen the price of pure thiamine come down from $400 a gram to 6 cents. Something similar can be done with every chemical which the human body needs in quantities of a gram a day or less; if scores or hundreds of grams are needed daily, the substance must be grown, not synthesized.*

If such a policy is followed—as it proves feasible—we shall greatly aid the farmer by permitting him to raise those crops which give the largest yields. In my opinion it is visionary to contemplate introducing into the most densely populated areas of the world the diversified type of agriculture which characterizes Denmark and Wisconsin. To attempt to meet the world's food problems by that type of measure to the exclusion of artificial aids is to sell out to Communism in this generation and to bow to Malthus in the succeeding one.

* R. R. Williams, "Chemistry as a Supplement to Agriculture in Meeting World Food Needs." *American Scientist 44,* 317 (1956).

1

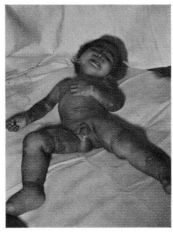

2

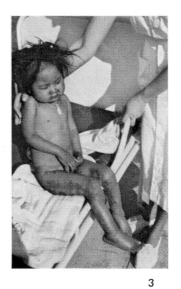

3

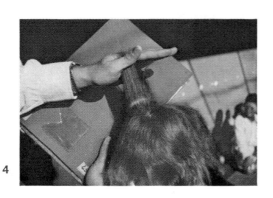

4

5

6

Kwashiorkor in Many Lands

Exfoliative dermatitis is conspicuous alike in South Africa (1) and (2), in San Salvador (3) and Guatemala (5). This child died a few days later. Light band in hair reflects previously active Kwashiorkor (4). Carried by their mothers on coffee-picking expeditions, these children, supposedly well, betray unmistakable signs of the same disease (San Salvador) (6).

ACKNOWLEDGMENTS

Grateful acknowledgments are made to the following who have kindly supplied me with pictures for illustrations: Bell Telephone Laboratories (Frontispiece), Drs. John F. Brock, Helen B. Burch, W. J. Darby, G. Garcia Pedroso, Grace A. Goldsmith, B. C. P. Jansen, C. G. King, E. J. Lease, Jorge Mardones, Eleanor D. Mason, C. R. Pascual, V. N. Patwardhan, N. S. Scrimshaw, A. Sreenivasan, Ta Cheng Tung, LeRoy Voris and Russell M. Wilder and Mrs. Louise F. Smith. I also wish to thank especially Dr. Sam C. Smith for much assistance in the preparation of the text, appendices and illustrations. All these and many other co-laborers in the field of nutrition have earned my undying gratitude and friendship.

R.R.W.

Williams–Waterman Fund Grants, 1940-1956

1. ANALYTICAL STUDIES

Grant No.	Date and Amount	Subject	Institution	Principal Investigators	Co-Workers	Results Reported
3	6/40 $515	Thiamine metabolism as revealed by radio-sulphur.	California Institute of Technology	Henry Borsook Don M. Yost	E. R. Buchman J. B. Hatcher Edwin McMillan	Metabolism is rapid, but some thiamine is retained as long as 36 days. Sulphur appears in neutral form and is inorganic sulphate. Losses of thiamine by excretion are inevitable.
5	7/40 $2,000 10/41 2,000	Cocarboxylase content of blood in infants.	University of Chicago	Elizabeth M. Knott F. W. Schultz	Sarah C. Kleiger	Thiamine content of human milk is 20 to 21 gammas per 100 cc. compared with 36 to 46 gammas for cow's milk.
11	2/41 $2,000 7/41 6,000 4/42 3,173	B_1 in human tissues.	Columbia University (later Harvard University)	J. W. Ferrebee	M. C. Hulse M. H. Carleen N. Weissman E. Stotz M. Clinton	Thiamine content of human tissues, Jour. Assn. for Research in Nervous and Mental Diseases 22, 42 (1943). Improvements in methodology and observations on thiaminase of carp.
20	6/41 $2,500	Microbiological methods of assay.	The University of Texas	R. J. Williams	E. E. Snell F. M. Strong Derrol Pennington H. K. Mitchell J. R. Mahan R. E. Eakin L. D. Wright Anne K. Stout R. C. Thompson V. H. Cheldelin	Such methods have been developed for 8 of the B vitamins, the W-W grant going to form a pool with funds from other sources.
24	3/42 $3,000	Excretion test for thiamine, riboflavin and nicotinic acid.	Johns Hopkins University	L. Emmett Holt	Victor A. Najjar Katherine C. Ketron	Improved thiochrome method for thiamine avoids errors due to F_2 in body fluids.
26	5/42 $3,000 8/44 1,500	Nutritive value of rice and its by-products.	University of Arkansas	M. C. Kik W. R. Horlacher	Floy B. Van Landingham	Effect of rice milling and rice conversion on the content of thiamine, niacin and riboflavin is reported. See N.R.C. Bulletin #112.

1. ANALYTICAL STUDIES (continued)

Grant No.	Date and Amount	Subject	Institution	Principal Investigators	Co-Workers	Results Reported
30	7/42 $2,500 7/43 3,000	Chemical nature of the fluorescent urinary ingredient known as F_2.	Johns Hopkins University	L. Emmett Holt	D. B. McNair Scott Virginia White	F_2 is a pyridine compound. It resembles N-methylnicotinamide but differs from it in some respects.
69	4/46 $3,500	Hydrolysis of proteins and amino acid content of vegetables and fruits.	University of Arizona	Arthur R. Kemmerer	—	Complete hydrolysis of proteins without loss of amino acids, especially tryptophan, was only partially successful. Tryptophan was determined in casein, carrots, broccoli and cauliflower.
86	5/47 $3,500 8/47 2,500 4/50 3,400	Chromatography of fatty acids.	Texas A. & M. College	Ralph T. Holman	W. T. Williams James H. Hagdahl	Chromatographic separations of individual fatty acids and certain sterols were effected.
93	11/47 $6,000	Investigation of methods of resolution of amino acids.	Iowa State College	Sidney W. Fox	R. B. Fearing	Resolution by adsorbents was unsuccessful. Use of 2-aminobutanol for resolution of glutamic acid and of methylated cinchonine for phenylalanine was fairly effective.
111	10/48 $4,000	Rapid method for determination of thiamine in rice.	Texas A. & M. College	P. B. Pearson	Carl M. Lyman	A rapid simple color test for thiamine is proposed.
113	9/48 $5,000 1/50 3,000 2/50 324	Thiamine in blood and urine of human adults.	Oregon State College	Clara A. Storvick	—	Only after extended repetitions was it possible to secure reliable and consistent thiamine values in blood by the method of Burch.
138	4/50 $1,800 4/52 3,500 6/53 3,500	Determination of purines, pyrimidines, nucleotides and nucleosides.	University of California	M. S. Dunn	Richard Zuckerman Edward Geller	Thymidine was isolated and preparations were made of desoxyribodepolymerase, phosphatase, nucleoside phosphorylase and guanine desoxyriboside.
185	7/52 $10,000 12/52 36 2/52 14 3/53 823 4/53 963 5/53 80	Analysis of Cuban foods and dietaries.	Fundacion de Investigaciones Medicas (FIM)	—	Robert S. Harris Juan Navia Hady Lopez Margarita Cimadevilla Edelmira Fernandez	275 Cuban foods have been analyzed for 5 vitamins, 3 amino acids and other nutrients. (See text, page 40.)
188	7/52 $5,000	Trace elements in biological systems.	Harvard Medical School	Bert L. Vallee	—	Spectrophotometric methods for estimating copper, strontium, iron, zinc, aluminum, manganese and several of the heavy metals have been greatly refined.

No.	Dates	Amount	Project	Institution	Director	Associates	Progress
206	12/54 1955 2/56 3/56 4/56	$4,760 12,834 3,360 3,360 148	Evaluation of protein quality of Philippine food plants and other protein foods.	Institute of Nutrition, Manila, Philippines	Conrado R. Pascual	——	Microbiological assays of 20 Philippine foods for all essential and sulphur-containing amino acids, except tryptophan, have been completed. Animal feeding assays will follow in all disputable cases.
206-A	1955 2/55 3/56	$2,777 2,100 1,500	Evaluation of protein quality of Philippine food plants and other protein foods.	University of the Philippines	Augusto Tenmatay	——	Chromatographic verification has been made of all the results reported on Grant #206.
207	12/54	$4,000	Analysis of Pacific islands foods with particular reference to their vitamin content.	South Pacific Commission, Noumea, New Caledonia	Sir Brian Freeston	F. Peters Miss Y. Macfarlane	The laboratory has been equipped and the analyses have been started.
215	4/55	$5,600	Metabolic reactions and assay methods for vitamin B_6.	Haskins Laboratories	S. H. Hutner	——	Work in progress.

2. BIOSYNTHESIS OF VITAMINS

No.	Dates	Amount	Project	Institution	Director	Associates	Progress
25	3/42 7/43	$1,000 1,050	Isolation of alkali sensitive precursor of nicotinic acid from wheat.	University of Wisconsin	F. M. Strong	W. A. Krehl	A precursor of nicotinic acid occurs in cereals. It becomes stimulatory for L. arabinosus after mild alkali treatment and is probably a nicotinic acid derivative bearing acidic groups attached to the carboxyl. Methods of estimating the precursor are described.
64	5/46 5/47 3/48 4/49 6/50 5/51 5/52	$3,000 3,000 4,000 4,000 4,000 4,000 4,000	Tryptophan metabolism and interconversions of aromatic metabolites.	California Institute of Technology	H. K. Mitchell G. W. Beadle	B. N. Ames H. S. Forrest J. F. Nyc Wm. Drell E. Liefer W. H. Langham F. A. Haskins	Phenylalanine can replace tryptophan in a Neurospora mutant. It is converted into anthranilic acid in wild Neurospora. Isotopic N experiments confirm conversion of hydroxy-anthranilic acid into nicotinic acid. Kynurenine is an intermediate between tryptophan and nicotinic acid. Later work involved the isolation of new pteridines and precursors of the flavins.
77	2/47 12/47 6/48 9/48 7/49 6/50	$3,700 1,900 3,800 2,000 3,800 3,800	Biosynthesis of nicotinic acid.	Yale University	David M. Bonner	W. A. Krehl C. Yanofsky O. E. Landman C. W. H. Partridge Elga Wasserman	Tryptophan tagged with N^{15} yields niacin so tagged. Pyridoxine is required to convert anthranilic acid to niacin. Hydroxyanthranilic acid in large doses serves in lieu of niacin in the rat. Acetyl kynurenine has a low niacin effect. Indole→tryptophan→kynurenine→hydroxykynurenine→hydroxyanthranilic acid→intermediate→niacin is an established pathway. ↓ quinolinic acid

2. BIOSYNTHESIS OF VITAMINS (continued)

Grant No.	Date and Amount	Subject	Institution	Principal Investigators	Co-Workers	Results Reported
94	12/47 $3,700	Qualitative and quantitative relationships between tryptophan and niacin and the "pellagragenic agent" in corn.	Amherst College	George W. Kidder	Virginia C. Dewey	Tetrahymena is unlike the rat and chick since it cannot synthesize niacin from tryptophan. Wolley's "pellagragenic agent" does not produce niacin deficiency in tetrahymena.
112	10/48 $1,800	Nicotinic acid metabolism.	Duke University	W. A. Perlzweig	Philip Handler Irwin Leder Murray Heimberg Sylvia Hunter	Pyridoxine is not directly involved in conversion of tryptophan to N-methyl nicotinamide by the rat. The fate of niacin in man, rat, dog, pig, rabbit, guinea pig, goat, sheep and calf is disclosed.
117	1/49 $3,800	Relation between D-amino acids and biosynthesis of thiamine.	Amherst College	George W. Kidder	Virginia C. Dewey	Tetrahymena can synthesize thiamine under certain conditions pointing to an unknown factor supplied by protogen.
226	4/56 $3,170	Biosynthesis of thiamine.	University of Chicago	Daniel L. Harris	—	Work in progress.

3. CEREAL ENRICHMENT PROJECTS

Grant No.	Date and Amount	Subject	Institution	Principal Investigators	Co-Workers	Results Reported
33	8/42 to 3/56 $168,500	Improvement of the nutritive value of certain staple southern foods.	Clemson Agricultural College	E. J. Lease	R. C. Ringrose	Whole corn enrichment has become obligatory by law in South Carolina and Alabama and is widely practiced voluntarily in North Carolina and Georgia. Effective July 1, 1956, a law requires that all rice sold in South Carolina must be fortified with thiamine, niacin and iron; calcium and riboflavin are optional added ingredients. (See text, pages 54, 56 and 57.)
51	8/44 $1,500	Nutritional survey in Newfoundland.	Peter Bent Brigham Hospital	Fredrick J. Stare	J. Metcoff A. J. McQueeney	Results reported under Grant #53.
53	8/44 $2,200	Nutritional survey in Newfoundland.	New York Post Graduate Medical School and Hospital	Ellen McDevitt Robert Dove Grace Goldsmith	Margaret A. Dove	40% of the poorer element of Norris Point, 113 persons, were examined. Remedial measures were indicated for 92% of the women, 88% of men, 70% of pre-school children and 58% of pre-adolescents. Deficiencies of vitamin A, riboflavin (also iron and hemoglobin in the women) were prevalent. (See text, page 54.)

No.	Dates	Amount	Project	Institution	Investigator(s)		Description
66	1/46 2/47 3/47 11/47	$6,000 1,000 2,000 421	Value of cereal enrichment.	The University of Texas	Jet C. Winters	—	Variation of cereal non-cereal ratio in diets for rats imitative of human diets revealed a greater advantage for enrichment in proportion to cereal content.
84	3/47 6/48 12/48 3/50 5/51 8/52 6/55	$25,000 12,500 12,500 25,000 35,000 35,000 5,000	Enriched rice and beriberi in Bataan province.	Institute of Nutrition, Manila, Philippines	Juan Salcedo, Jr. Eufronio O. Carrasco	—	A successful demonstration of the efficacy of enriched rice as shown by clinical surveys of incidence, by biochemical analyses, and by mortality records before and after its introduction. (See text, pages 62, 64, 65 and 66.)
84-B	3/50	$25,000	Purchase and installation of feeders and mixing equipment—Bataan project.	National Rice and Corn Corp. (NARIC), Manila, Philippines	—		Enrichment feeders were provided and installed in several hundred mills in Tarlac and Pangasinanan provinces.
85	6/47 6/48	$7,000 4,000	Nutritional significance of the use of enriched flour and cereals.	Kansas State College	Beulah D. Westerman		Rats fed mixtures of natural foods including enriched versus unenriched flour exhibited superior growth and reproduction in the former case.
95	12/47	$6,000	Enrichment of corn meal in Alabama mills.	Alabama Polytechnic Institute	P. O. Davis		During 1948-49 a vigorous county-by-county campaign resulted in the installation of feeders in 481 grist mills in 64 out of 67 counties in Alabama affording substantially full enrichment of all corn meal, all under the leadership of John P. Bell.
					Dorothy R. Linn Frances Templeton Ruth I. Wells Harriet A. Harlan		
					John P. Bell		
108	7/47 4/48	$800 4,400	Nutritional re-survey of Newfoundland.	Tulane University	Grace A. Goldsmith		A continuation of Grants 51 and 53 showing a very substantial decline in 1948 of the deficiency symptoms which were apparent in 1944 before the introduction of bread and flour enrichment. (See text, page 54.)
109	9/48 6/50 9/50	$6,150 200 4,150	Nutrition re-survey in Bataan.	Columbia University	Helen B. Burch		Biochemical findings on 200 people before and after introduction of rice enrichment in Bataan, showed significant increases in thiamine of blood and urine and of hemoglobin. Vitamin C of blood remained unchanged at a low level. (See Grant #84.)
114	1/49 6/50	$5,000 3,768	Enrichment of corn meal in Mississippi mills.	Mississippi State College	L. I. Jones	—	Unfortunate choice of a "corn enrichment specialist" resulted in very little accomplishment.

3. CEREAL ENRICHMENT PROJECTS (continued)

Grant No.	Date and Amount	Subject	Institution	Principal Investigators	Co-Workers	Results Reported
116	7/49 $3,700 12/49 4,730	Regional extension of corn meal enrichment.	Alabama Polytechnic Institute	P. O. Davis	—	Discussions of corn meal enrichment with agricultural extension services of all Southern states except Kentucky. Many were not ready to undertake it; some such as Oklahoma, Arkansas and Texas felt corn consumption is too scattered; Georgia and Mississippi were more interested.
136	2/50 to 3/56 $64,000	Enrichment of bread and flour and the fortification of rice in Cuba.	Fundacion de Investigaciones Medicas (FIM)	Louise F. Smith	—	Much popular interest has been aroused as indicated by increasing attendance at food fairs each year, but endeavors to secure enrichment legislation have not yet succeeded. (See text, page 73.)
152	6/51 $7,350 7/52 6,350 5/53 4,000 5/54 4,000 6/55 3,000	Corn enrichment in Georgia.	University of Georgia	C. C. Murray	C. B. Earnest John Noland	Progressive numbers of mills are enriching corn meal in Georgia. The total at the end of 1955 was 114 mills, producing about 80% of corn meal in the state.
155	10/51 $7,000	Corn enrichment program in North Carolina.	North Carolina State College	David S. Weaver	—	No suitable enrichment specialist has yet been found to undertake systematic work. Educational work has proceeded but legislation about whole corn enrichment has not yet been enacted.
156	6/51 $2,660 ($2,579 refunded)	Enrichment of corn meal in Mississippi mills.	Mississippi State College	M. S. Shaw	—	Project discontinued as of 12/31/51 since previous mistakes set a very bad precedent and made the work ineffective. (See Grant #114.)
163	7/52 $ 500 7/52 358 9/52 127 9/52 807 7/53 1,141 3/54 28 5/54 2	Enrichment of white rice in Formosa.	National Taiwan University, Taipei	Ta Cheng Tung	—	78 families participating in an experiment with enriched rice (with and without riboflavin) exhibited improvement in nutritional status with respect to thiamine and hemoglobin levels, also a reduction of stomatitis in cases where riboflavin was included. Similar experiments are now under way in two normal schools.
164	12/51 $15,000	Rice enrichment survey of Bataan by WHO-FAO survey team.	Food & Agriculture Organization of the United States	W. R. Aykroyd	—	Report published as Rice Enrichment in the Philippines, F.A.O. Nutritional Studies No. 12, 1954.

No.	Date	Amount	Project	Institution	Investigator	Co-investigator	Notes
172	4/52 3/53 8/53 4/54 12/54	$6,000 5,500 2,500 3,400 2,000	Study of pellagra in Yugoslavia.	Vanderbilt University School of Medicine	William J. Darby	—	In an area where pellagra is highly prevalent, corn meal enrichment was inaugurated by South Carolina techniques in 17 small mills. A major decline in the incidence of pellagra was noted two years later. (See text, page 31.)
173	4/52	$2,200	Enrichment of whole ground corn meal and diets.	Mississippi State College	Dorothy Dickins Olive Sheets	—	84% of 429 farm families use whole corn at the rate of 2.4 pounds per capita per week compared with 2.0 pounds of flour. Enrichment of whole corn meal would have permitted more low income families to meet NRC's recommended allowances, especially niacin.
192	5/53	$5,000	Investigation of the nutritional value of iron preparations added to enriched bread.	Cornell University	Frances A. Johnston	Shirley Friend Marita Leland	The percentage of iron absorbed from reduced iron, ferrous sulphate and ferric phosphate were, respectively, 2, 4 and 3. Individual variations were considerable.

4. DIETS

No.	Date	Amount	Project	Institution	Investigator	Co-investigator	Notes
19	6/41 7/42	$2,000 1,691	Vitamin content of Southwestern diets.	The University of Texas	Jet C. Winters Ruth Leslie	—	Scanty intakes of several nutrients, especially vitamin A and riboflavin, were revealed.
37	2/43	$7,500	Nutrition in industry.	California Institute of Technology	Henry Borsook	—	Vitamin supplementation was given to a group of aircraft workers for 1 year. One control group was given a placebo and a third group received no special treatment. The vitamin group showed lower absenteeism, less turnover and higher merit review than the other groups in the second 6 months of the year.
99	1/48 1/49	$5,000 5,000	Child growth study.	New York University	Norman Jolliffe	—	103 underweight children were divided into two matched groups, one of which received supplements of A and D the first year, and in addition thiamine, riboflavin, niacin and ascorbic acid the second year. No increase in rate of growth or mental development was found.
107	6/48 4/49 4/50 5/51	$3,000 3,000 3,000 3,000	Long term effects of diets.	Columbia University	Henry C. Sherman	—	Even a diet so good as to permit growing 76 generations of rats is capable of further improvement by additions of calcium, vitamin A or milk.

4. DIETS (continued)

Grant No.	Date and Amount	Subject	Institution	Principal Investigators	Co-Workers	Results Reported
178	4/52 $1,000	Effect of dietary essentials on the growth of rats maintained on a typical South Indian diet.	Northwestern University	Paul S. Rhoads	R. Arulanantham	An extension of work carried on at Women's Christian College, Madras, India.
186	10/52 $4,250 2/54 2,500 6/54 1,164	a) Vitamin B_1 deficiencies in the population. b) Nutritive value of Pakistani foodstuffs with respect to vitamin B factors.	National West Regional Laboratories, Lahore, Pakistan	Bashir Ahmad	M. D. Chugtai	Dietary surveys for all major nutrients have been made in two groups of families; losses of thiamine and riboflavin in cooking have been determined; losses in vitamins in perspiration and effect of fasting during Ramzan were studied.
200	2/54 $5,000 4/55 5,000 2/56 5,000	Investigation of the nutritional status of persons consuming a predominantly corn diet (Guatemala and Mexico).	Pan American Sanitary Bureau	Nevin S. Scrimshaw	R. L. Squibb J. Edgar Braham Guillermo Arroyave	Process of preparing tortillas results in loss of niacin. However, rats fed tortillas grow better than when given raw corn. Addition of niacin to either ration gives better growth, and difference between groups disappears. Efforts to demonstrate a toxic factor in corn were unsuccessful. Biochemical studies of kwashiorkor cases are in progress. (See text, page 36.)
210	10/54 $3,800 12/55 5,200	Life span and diet.	Washington University	Martin Silberberg Ruth Silberberg	—	Work in progress.

5. EDUCATION AND PUBLICATION

Grant No.	Date and Amount	Subject	Institution	Principal Investigators	Co-Workers	Results Reported
28	6/42 $2,000	Conference on dietary diseases.	Clemson Agricultural College	E. J. Lease	—	Conference in Birmingham, Ala., May 23, 1942, set the stage for cooperation in corn enrichment in southern states.
67	1/46 to 3/56 $75,000	Support of work of Food and Nutrition Board.	National Research Council	—	—	—
71	5/46 $5,000	Support of public health nutrition program in Florida.	Florida State Board of Health	Walter Wilkins	—	Hemoglobin levels in school children vary during the course of the day. Supplementary iron alone does not increase borderline hemoglobins in a hookworm area but does increase those with very low levels.

No.	Date	Amount	Project	Institution	Investigator	Associates	Results
83	7/47	$1,465	Exhibit at American Medical Association convention, "Signs of Nutritional Deficiency Diseases."	New York University	Norman Jolliffe	—	An excellent exhibit of educational value was provided.
89	7/47	$1,725	Construction of food exhibit and sponsorship of city-wide contest in public schools on nutrition exhibits.	New York City Food and Nutrition Commission	Norman Jolliffe	—	Valuable educational results were achieved.
131	8/49	$2,500	Publication of "The Biology of Human Starvation."	University of Minnesota	Ancel Keys	—	Book was published in 1950.
165	12/51	$3,350	Publication of "Administrative Practices of Public Health Nutrition Services."	American Public Health Association, Inc.	Reginald T. Atwater	—	The manual has been published.
205	7/54	$8,850	Completion of the publication of research performed under the Children's Fund of Michigan.	Merrill-Palmer School	Icie Macy Hoobler	—	Publication in progress.

6. ENZYME STUDIES

No.	Date	Amount	Project	Institution	Investigator	Associates	Results
10	1940	$2,500	Investigations on the role of vitamin B_1.	California Institute of Technology	E. R. Buchman	James Bonner Erik Heegard N. H. Horowitz	A pyruvic acid decarboxylase from pea roots was studied as to characteristics and mode of action.
21	1/42 1/43	$8,090 6,190	Intermediate carbohydrate metabolism.	New York University	Severo Ochoa	—	Dependence of pyruvate oxidation on mechanism of generation of phosphate bond energy was revealed.
50	3/44 3/45 8/46 8/47	$5,000 5,000 5,000 5,000	Isolation of enzymes with more than one catalytic function.	Columbia University	David E. Green	P. K. Stumpf K. Zarudnaya S. Ratner M. Blanchard V. Nocito-Carroll	The oxidation of fatty acids, amino acids, glutamic acid and proline funnel into the cyclophorase system which catalyses the oxidation of pyruvic acid to carbon dioxide and water.
55	8/44 9/45	$3,400 4,000	Biological oxidation of pyruvic acid.	New York University	Severo Ochoa	E. Weisz-Tabori Morton Schneider A. Kornberg Alan Mehler	Enzymes of carbon dioxide assimilation were compared and studied.
80	4/47	$4,000	Antithiamine activity of plant materials.	Oregon State College	J. R. Haag	P. H. Weswig V. H. Freed	Bracken fern contains an enzyme which destroys thiamine in cattle which eat it, inducing polyneuritis. Steaming destroys it but no practicable antidote applicable in pastures was found.

6. ENZYME STUDIES (continued)

Grant No.	Date and Amount	Subject	Institution	Principal Investigators	Co-Workers	Results Reported
90	7/47 $5,000	Biochemistry of thiamine destroying or Chastek paralysis enzyme.	Iowa State College	R. R. Sealock S. W. Fox	—	Several inhibitors of thiaminase were found. O-aminobenzyl pyridium salts are activators. The thiaminase of bracken fern is similar to that of clams. The function of the aminase remains unknown.
101	2/48 $1,500	Enzymatic mechanisms of amino nitrogen transfer and urea formation.	New York University	Sarah Ratner	—	Two enzymes have been isolated which successively function to form arginine from citrulline in two steps. The first requires high energy phosphate.
121	5/49 $3,600 6/50 2,400 5/51 3,600 7/52 3,600 5/54 3,600 6/55 3,600	a) Inositol as a constituent of pancreatic amylase. b) Amino acid composition of pancreatic amylase.	Columbia University	Mary L. Caldwell	—	Amylase contains 20 amino acids and no non-protein prosthetic group. Free amino groups furnished by lysine are essential to its activity.
132	10/49 $5,000	a) Reduction of cytochrome by pyridine nucleotides as catalyzed by flavins. b) Action of riboflavin analogs on isolated enzymes.	Western Reserve University	Thomas P. Singer	Edna B. Kearney	Riboflavin analogs do not function in true competitive fashion over wide concentrations. Riboflavin inhibits snake venom L-amino acid oxidase. The latter contains flavin adenine dinucleotide as the prosthetic group. Flavo-kinase was isolated from yeast. Alpha-carboxylase (diphosphothiamine is prosthetic group), isolated from wheat germ, catalyzes decarboxylation of a-keto acids, formation of ketols from aldehydes or from aldehydes and a-keto acids.
141	6/50 $4,500 6/51 5,350 7/52 5,420 6/53 2,500	Enzymatic mechanisms in trans-methylation.	Western Reserve University	G. L. Cantoni	D. G. Anderson P. J. Vignos J. Baddiley G. A. Jamieson E. Scarano	Adenosine triphosphate acts on methionine to produce S-adenosyl methionine (I), an important intermediate in transmethylations. (I) reacts with homocysteine to produce adenosyl homocysteine; with guanidoacetate it yields creatine. It has been synthesized. The enzymes concerned are described.
144	10/50 $4,500 6/51 903	Tissue metabolism as it concerns the breakdown of carbohydrates.	University of Pennsylvania	Otto Meyerhof	D. Wright Wilson Ann Kaplan Harry Green	This study, aimed at relating energy of bonds to reactivity, was brought to a close by Dr. Meyerhof's death.

No.	Date	Amount	Project	Institution	Principal Investigator	Associates	Description
147	5/51 5/52 7/52 6/53	$3,000 3,300 900 3,550	Function and nature of bound enzymes.	Johns Hopkins University	Nathan O. Kaplan Sidney P. Colowick	T. P. Wang L. J. Zatman M. M. Ciotti A. Nason H. A. Oldewurtel L. Shuster R. M. Burton M. E. Pullman	Apart from purification of various enzymes, the study has been extended to isonicotinic acid hydrazide on the theory that analog formation may be involved in the action of the drug.
148	5/51 4/52 3/53	$3,000 3,700 2,300	Enzymatic functions of oleic acid.	University of Minnesota	Herman C. Lichstein	R. B. Boyd	An enzymatic basis was sought to explain the vitamin-like activity of certain fatty acids but without conclusive results.
151	6/51	$3,250	Enzyme systems involved in biological oxidations and syntheses.	New York University	Severo Ochoa	J. R. Stern M. J. Coon A. del Campillo I. Zelitch	The oxidation of ketoglutarate is responsible for converting acetoacetate to a coenzyme A derivative. The study has thrown much light on fatty acid metabolism.
190	3/53 5/54 6/55 3/56 9/53	$4,845 5,860 4,860 5,000 2,100	Riboflavin enzymes.	Washington University	Helen B. Burch	———	Seven enzymes containing riboflavin have been determined by micro methods, and the role of these enzymes in various organs is under study.
197	9/53	$2,000	Oxidative metabolism in acetic acid bacteria.	Oregon State College	Vernon H. Cheldelin	Jens G. Hauge Tsoo E. King R. W. Newburgh C. A. Claridge	These bacteria derive energy from glycerol via the pentose cycle. The Krebs cycle appears to be absent.
199	1/54	$4,700	In vitro metabolism of carbohydrate in liver.	University of Chile	Hermann Niemeyer	———	Dinitrophenol inhibits glycogen synthesis by rat liver. DL-glyceraldehyde reduced glycogen formation by rat diaphragm. Studies are still in progress.
201	2/54 9/55	$5,500 5,500	The succinate-glycine cycle: The mechanism of formation of porphyrins, purines, serine and methyl groups.	Columbia University	David Shemin	———	An enzyme from duck blood converts delta-aminolevulinic acid (I) to pyrrole. The conversion of pyrrole to protoporphyrin is being pursued. 3 carbon atoms of uric acid are derived from the carbon bearing the amino group in (I).
211	11/54 10/55	$3,275 3,000	Enzymatic and regulatory mechanisms in ketone body formation and utilization.	Western Reserve University	Joseph R. Stern	———	Metal chelates of acetoacetyl-S-CoA and the enzymatic recemization of beta-hydroxy butyryl-S-CoA have been studied. An alternate fatty acid oxidation cycle using thioesters of pantetheine and enzymes the same as or similar to those of the CoA cycle has been found.

6. ENZYME STUDIES (continued)

Grant No.	Date and Amount	Subject	Institution	Principal Investigators	Co-Workers	Results Reported
212	1/55 $5,600	Single carbon unit metabolism.	University of Texas	William Shive	Joanne Olivard, Robert H. Trubey	Work in progress.
222	12/55 $3,695	Pathways and compounds of intermediary metabolism.	New York University College of Medicine	Gerhard W. E. Plaut	—	Work in progress.

7. FATS

Grant No.	Date and Amount	Subject	Institution	Principal Investigators	Co-Workers	Results Reported
52	10/45 $3,900 4/47 3,900	Parenteral nutrition.	Harvard School of Public Health	Fredrick J. Stare	—	Animal experiments on the utilization of emulsified fat given intravenously culminated in 1948 with the first successful use of intravenous fat in a human patient.
118	1/49 $2,500	Fatty acid metabolism in scurvy.	Duke University	Frederick Bernheim	Karl M. Wilbur	Preliminary indications that linoleic acid retards development of scurvy in guinea pigs failed to be confirmed.
125	5/49 $2,400 4/50 2,400 6/51 3,600	Lipid biosynthesis through use of neurospora mutants.	Syracuse University	Joseph Lein	P. S. Lein, D. C. Appleby, A. Gourevitch, T. A. Puglisi	Techniques were developed for preparation of pure fatty acids. In neurospora the unsaturated fatty acids are synthesized by a different pathway than saturated ones.
139	6/50 $2,200	Pyridoxine and thiamine deficiencies in fat metabolism.	Massachusetts Institute of Technology	Robert S. Harris	Henry Sherman	The effects of these two deficiencies upon arachidonic acid metabolism are due to inanition rather than specific causes.
181	5/52 $3,000	Lipid metabolism in atherosclerosis and disease with abnormal serum lipids.	Yale University	William F. VanEck	—	Analytical methods for cholesterol esters in the serum have been perfected. Diabetic subjects on a fat-free diet exhibit a remarkable drop in serum lipids and increase in glucose tolerance.
209	9/54 $4,300	Biotin-oleic acid interrelationship in micro-organisms.	Louisiana State University	Virginia R. Williams	Shichi Suzuki	Work in progress.
221	12/55 $2,500	Effect of ingestion of highly unsaturated animal fat upon serum lipide concentrations in patients.	Rockefeller Institute for Medical Research	E. H. Ahrens	—	Work in progress.

8. MEDICAL APPLICATIONS OF NUTRITIONAL PRINCIPLES

No.	Dates	Amount	Subject	Institution	Director	Associates	Description
12	2/41 1/42	$3,200 3,500	Relation of pyruvic acid tolerance to B₁ intake.	New York University	Norman Jolliffe	E. Bueding, H. Wortis, M. H. Stein, R. Goodhart, W. Goldfarb, Y. A. Fazekas, H. Herrlich, H. E. Himwich	Blood pyruvate curves are elevated following ingestion of glucose, and in thiamine deficiency this elevation is prolonged. J. Biol. Chem. 140, 697 (1941).
22	4/42 4/43	$3,500 3,500	Biochemistry of nutrition in rheumatic fever.	Columbia University	A. F. Coburn, D. E. Green	—	Rheumatic fever children were protected against further attacks on diets involving high animal protein; eggs, milk, meat, etc.
34	2/43 10/43	$1,000 1,500	Intestinal absorption in deficiency diseases.	Western Reserve University	Victor C. Myers	J. R. Leonards, A. H. Free, A. J. Beams	Acute deficiency of thiamine or the B complex reduces absorption of galactose from the gut. Most other deficiencies do not reduce absorption. Penicillin is not effective in suppressing intestinal synthesis in the rat sufficiently to produce deficiency signs.
35	11/43 3/44 8/44 2/45	$1,000 525 300 950	Niacin deficiency in infants and children.	New York University	Harry Bakwin	James Winn, Margaret Tenbrinck, Helen Seibert	Supposed normal children, exhibiting tongue lesions, respond very gradually to dosage with niacinamide (200 to 400 mgs. max.) with favorable effects on appetite. In many cases, tongue lesions persist as long as 3 years. Urine studies indicate lower levels of F_2 for infants than for older children and adults.
38	2/43 1944	$2,780 3,900	Survey of nutritional status of low income group of ambulatory patients and response to specific therapy	New York University	Norman Jolliffe	Rita M. Most, Ernest Bueding, M. H. Stein, H. Wortis	The responses to vitamin therapy of 130 patients exhibiting a variety of deficiency symptoms were followed for two years. Most symptoms cleared; a few persisted in milder forms; of these very few responded further to yeast therapy.
42	7/43	$1,400	The effect of administering amino acids to severe burn cases.	New York University	Frank Co Tui	M. J. Vinvi, A. M. Wright, J. J. Mulholland, I. Borcham	Three cases of second and third degree burns were successfully treated with protein hydrolysates which appear to promote nutrition of tissues in the area of injury.
57	10/45 to 6/55	$88,500	Clinical investigation of nutritional diseases.	Tulane University	Grace A. Goldsmith	—	See text, page 26.

8. MEDICAL APPLICATIONS OF NUTRITIONAL PRINCIPLES (continued)

Grant No.	Date and Amount	Subject	Institution	Principal Investigators	Co-Workers	Results Reported
76	12/46 $12,500 3/48 10,000 1/49 10,000 4/49 2,500 1/50 12,500 12/51 12,500 12/52 6,000	Significance of nutrition and nutritional deficiencies in pregnancy.	Pennsylvania Hospital Nutrition Research Clinic	Winslow T. Tompkins	——	A systematic study was made during 1946-1953 of the nutritional status of hundreds of mothers during pregnancy in relation to successful clinical management of maternity cases.
82	4/47 $122	Relationship of pantothenic acid deficiency in mice to syndrome of "burning feet" in humans.	Columbia University	Murray Glusman	——	Work was abandoned after initial studies.
88	6/47 $5,680 12/48 5,680 11/49 5,680	Disturbances of nutrition associated with diseases in infants and children.	University of Minnesota	Charles D. May	——	The commonest cause of intestinal malabsorption in children leading to steatorrhea was thought to be intolerance of starches. Attempts to reproduce this condition in monkeys were not successful.
97	1/48 $5,000 1/49 5,000 12/49 5,000 1/51 5,000 12/51 5,000 12/52 5,000 2/54 2,383	Morphologic characterization of deficiency states and of certain "hypervitaminoses."	Children's Hospital, Boston	S. Burt Wolbach	Charlotte Maddock Stephen Maddock Jonathan Cohen John Craig P. Lacroix S. Farber L. Uzman C. S. Petty	Our grant aided in support of a wide ranging program of research on many topics, among which were hypervitaminosis A, rickets, scurvy, galactosemia and collagen diseases. (See text, page 28.)
115	1/49 $3,000 4/49 2,000	Relationship between deficiency of vitamin K during pregnancy and intracranial hemorrhage at birth.	State University of Iowa Medical School	P. C. Jeans	Kirsten Toverud R. R. Rembolt	Because of changes in staff and the death of Dr. Toverud, the original objectives had to be modified. Reports were rendered on the incidence of congenital abnormalities in infants in relation to protein intakes of mothers during pregnancy. The diets of rural women were analyzed.
133	1/50 $5,159	Histochemistry of Laennec's cirrhosis of the liver.	New York University	Joseph Post	——	Needle biopsy specimens of diseased human liver differ characteristically from animal liver or post-mortem human liver in respect to ribosenucleic acid. Such diseased liver lacks a pigment found in normal human liver.

No.	Date	Amount	Project	Institution	Investigator	Associates	Results
166	12/51	$3,000	Group management of obesity.	Nutrition Clinics Fund	Norman Jolliffe	——	The value of group management of obese patients has been demonstrated.
167	7/52	$5,252	The beriberi problem and its control in Northern Circars.	Madras Public Health Department	K. S. Viswanathan	——	The laboratory has been set up, but no data have been received.
168	12/51	$2,750	Cytologic alterations in riboflavin deficiency.	University of Vermont	Ephraim Woll	——	A technique was developed for detecting early signs of riboflavin deficiency by the histology of tongue scrapings.
177	4/52 3/53 5/54 6/55	$4,800 4,800 4,800 5,996	Study of the metabolic role of vitamin E in the prevention of liver injury.	University of Pittsburgh	Robert E. Olson	C. S. Yang M. Riegl B. Stewart	Vitamin E affords protection to rats against hepatic necrosis in a non-specific manner. The synthesis of coenzyme A is diminished in conditions leading to necrosis. Studies are continuing.
204	6/54 1/55 9/55	$4,005 3,955 2,465	Survey of the vitamins in the cerebrospinal fluid in multiple sclerosis.	Mt. Sinai Hospital New York City	Harry Sobotka	——	B_{12} and folic acid have been determined in 40 cases. 3 of 6 cases of multiple sclerosis exhibit very high B_{12} values.
227	4/56	$4,800	Partial and latent vitamin B_{12} deficiencies and vitamin B_{12} absorption defects in man.	New York Medical College	George B. Jerzy Glass	——	Work in progress.

9. NEW FACTORS IN NUTRITION

No.	Date	Amount	Project	Institution	Investigator	Associates	Results
4	8/40	$4,000	Uncharacterized members of vitamin B complex.	University of California	T. H. Jukes S. H. Babcock		An active fraction from yeast increases survival of chicks on diets containing all known nutritional factors, including para aminobenzoic acid, inositol, biotin, choline and pantothenic acid. (Concerns early study of folic acid.)
18	1941 2/42 6/42 4/43 11/43 11/44	$3,500 250 4,000 2,000 7,550 7,700	New vitamin present in unpasteurized cream.	Oregon State College	Rosalind Wulzen		Attempts at isolation were unsuccessful due to quantitative inadequacy of the test with guinea pigs. Physiological and biochemical changes resulting from deficiency of the factor were studied.
47	10/43 9/44 2/46	$1,200 1,800 2,500	Lactobacillus gayoni 8289 factor.	Oregon State College	Vernon Cheldelin	T. R. Riggs H. F. Sarrett R. C. Wooster A. Kornberg	1,000 fold concentration of the factor from liver was achieved. Liver also contains a growth factor for Leuconostoc mesenteroides P-60 which was concentrated 1,000 fold. Further results under Grant #63.

9. NEW FACTORS IN NUTRITION (continued)

Grant No.	Date and Amount	Subject	Institution	Principal Investigators	Co-Workers	Results Reported
63	10/49 $1,800	New growth factors for lactic acid bacteria.	Oregon State College	Vernon Cheldelin	—	B_{12} is identical with the original L. gayoni factor. However, cultures kept for 2 years develop a need for another factor which is of a nucleotide nature. The Leuconostoc mesenteroides factor of Grant #47 turned out to be pyridoxamine or pyridoxal phosphate.
72	6/46 $1,400 6/47 1,400 6/48 1,800 6/49 1,800	Nutritional factors involved in growth and metabolism.	University of Wisconsin	Esmond E. Snell	E. J. Herbst H. Kihara	Systematic studies of several factors influencing the nutrition of a score of organisms were carried out in 1946–51. Several new nutrilites were revealed.
74	11/46 $7,500 10/47 6,000	Isolation of the antianemic substance of liver.	University of Alabama	J. K. Cline	R. B. Johnson	Folic acid deficiency promotes anemia in rats and increases the thiamine requirement. Pyridoxine deficiency also promotes anemia.
79	11/46 $2,000 10/47 2,000	New food accessory present in tomato juice.	Cornell University	D. C. Carpenter	—	Many attempts to isolate and define the substance were only partially successful. Work was concluded in 1951.
102	3/48 $4,200 5/49 4,300 4/50 4,200 6/51 4,500 7/52 4,500	a) Vitamin E and genital organs b) Vitamin A-like lard factor	Columbia University	C. A. Slanetz	—	Low pregnancy in vitamin E deficiency in rats is due to uterine rather than ovarian failure. The E requirement increases with age. The vitamin A-like action of lard is due to traces of vitamin A.
119	1/49 $2,300 12/49 700 4/50 500	Synthesis and biological testing of some new nucleosides.	University of Southern California	Donald W. Visser	—	5-chlorouridine, ribosylthiamine, ribosyl-5-methyl cytosine, and 5-(2', 5'-dichlorobenzeazo)-uridine were synthesized and tested on several micro-organisms and on mice.
146	5/51 $1,800 5/52 1,800	Function of putrescine and related compounds in metabolism of microbial and animal tissues.	University of Maryland	Edward J. Herbst	D. D. Hubbard	Putrescine, spermine and spermidine are essential vitamins for Hemophilus parainfluenzae. Putrescine functions in carbohydrate utilization.

10. NUTRITION IN RELATION TO MENTAL AND NERVOUS FUNCTION

No.	Dates	Amounts	Title	Institution	Investigator	Associate	Findings
6	8/40 9/41	$ 900 2,000	Protection by B vitamins of rats exposed to convulsions induced by auditory stimuli.	University of Pittsburgh	C. G. King H. W. Karn R. A. Patton	Ruth C. Wylie	Vitamin B_1 reduced convulsions; a combination of B_1, B_2 and B_6 reduced them more. Brewer's yeast was also effective. Jour. Comp. Psychology 31, 215 (1941).
15	7/41 7/42 4/43 11/43 1/44	$2,500 2,500 1,000 1,000 5,000	Effect of added thiamine on learning ability of children.	Columbia University	Ruth Harrell	Arthur I. Gates	Carefully matched pairs of children in an orphanage with a cheap but good dietary formed two groups, one of which received 2 mgs. of thiamine daily, the other a placebo. During 3 periods of 6 weeks, 1 year and 1 year, respectively, the former group excelled the latter in rate of learning of 8 out of 15 tests of skill and mental acuity.
23	3/43 10/43	$2,000 3,800	Action of thiamine in neuromuscular systems.	Harvard University	George Wald	Blanche Jackson Albert Wollenberger	Thiamine at pH 5 to 6 depresses the beat of Straub preparations of frog heart; so does cocarboxylase up to pH 7.6. Above pH 6 thiamine antagonizes acetylcholine; cocarboxylase does not. Deprivation of thiamine causes greatly increased activity in rats.
31	1942	$1,000	Influence of thiamine on the learning ability of the white rat.	University of Texas	Hugh C. Blodgett	—	No significant difference in maze learning ability could be found attributable to thiamine deficiency.
45	10/43 1944	$4,500 4,500	Glutamic acid in diseases of nervous system.	Columbia University	Heinrich Waelsch	—	DL- and L-glutamic acid are equally effective in petit mal. D-glutamic acid is found in urine after giving DL-. The acid-base balance is not shifted.
59	2/45 6/46 3/47 4/48 5/49 4/52 9/53	$6,000 6,000 6,000 6,000 6,000 3,550 400	Influence of prenatal diet on mentality of the young.	Columbia University	Ruth Harrell Arthur I. Gates	Ella Woodyard	Vitamin supplementation of poor women of Norfolk during pregnancy and of their offspring during first 5 years of life raised the I.Q. of children to a statistically significant degree. This effect was absent among Kentucky mountaineers.

10. NUTRITION IN RELATION TO MENTAL AND NERVOUS FUNCTION (continued)

Grant No.	Date and Amount	Subject	Institution	Principal Investigators	Co-Workers	Results Reported
60	5/45 $5,000 5/46 5,000	Glutamic acid in epilepsy.	Columbia University	Heinrich Waelsch	Blanche A. Prescott Ernest Borek Phyllis Sheiness Herbert K. Miller K. Albert P. Hoch Phyllis Owades J. C. Price	No differences in blood glutamic acid and glutamine were found between normal and epileptic patients. Glutamic acid reduces confusion of patients after electro-shock and increases I.Q. of retarded children. Methionine sulfoxide was found to be a specific antagonist of glutamic acid, and it, as well as other sulfoxides and sulfones, were studied in animals.
91	8/47 $4,400 6/48 3,900 7/49 1,650	Metabolism of isolated brain.	Columbia University	A. Geiger J. Magnes	R. M. Taylor	A surgical technique was developed for the perfusion of the brain of the living cat whereby the brain is chemically isolated from the rest of the body. A study of glutamine and glutamic acid in the brain in accord with Waelsch's findings was suggestive but inconclusive.
104	6/48 $5,600	Effects of glutamic acid upon learning ability in the albino rat.	Western State Psychiatric Institute and Clinic, Pittsburgh	Robert A. Patton	—	Inclusion of glutamic acid in the diet of rats did not increase the rate of learning of a water maze.

11. PHYSIOLOGY

Grant No.	Date and Amount	Subject	Institution	Principal Investigators	Co-Workers	Results Reported
27	1942 $4,400 3/44 2,000 9/46 250	Thiamine-pyruvate relationship in the mammalian organism.	Union University	H. E. Himwich	Annette Chester Edmund Homburger	By comparing arterial and venous blood of dogs, it was found that liver and heart remove pyruvate from the blood stream while other organs add it.
32	7/42 $2,000	Investigations on sulfonamides and thyroids.	Johns Hopkins University	E. V. McCollum	C. G. Mackenzie Julia Mackenzie	Sulfonamides or thioureas produce a lowering of the basal metabolic rate and enlargement of thyroids in rats, mice and dogs.
49	5/45 $3,400	Pyruvic acid cycle in anoxia.	Union University	H. E. Himwich	—	The heart in B_1 deficiency pours pyruvate into the blood stream and exhibits T wave changes which should be suspected as evidence of B_1 deficiency. Abnormalities were also observed in liver, muscle and intestine.

No.	Date	Amount	Title	Institution	Investigator		Description
92	10/47 9/48	$4,000 6,880	Metabolism of pyruvic acid in vivo.	Western Reserve University	Ernest Bueding Max Miller	—	Aspects of intermediary metabolism in tissues and micro-organisms previously investigated by in vitro techniques were substantiated in intact higher animals. Intravenous injection of pyruvate into dogs increases plasma citrate; glycine, fumarate, malate, succinate or glucose cause a rise of pyruvate in normal dogs, but not in humans with diabetes.
98	1/48 4/49 3/50 3/51	$1,500 1,500 1,500 1,500	Factors involved in excessive iron absorption on corn diets.	Harvard University	D. M. Hegsted Fredrick J. Stare	—	After study of high iron absorption by mice, guinea pigs and chicks, radio-iron studies made it clear that iron is constantly excreted in proportion to the body store.
100	1/48 4/49	$2,250 2,000	Glyconeogenesis induced by amino acids.	University of Oregon	W. R. Todd	Ellen Talman	Prefeeding of glycine to rats increases the respiratory quotients of the animals and induces a higher rate of glycogen formation in their diaphragms.
126	5/49 7/50	$4,450 3,100	Enzyme systems in peripheral tissues which undergo adaptive changes to diet.	University of Utah	Leo T. Samuels	—	The diaphragms of rats fed high-fat diets have a lower glucose metabolism than those fed high carbohydrate. Some substrate entering the Krebs cycle in competition with pyruvate is postulated. Octanoate is metabolized more rapidly by diaphragm from carbohydrate-fed than from fat-fed or fasted rats.
129	7/49	$3,500	Conversion of B-carotene to vitamin A in vitro.	Harvard University	George Wald	W. H. Yudkin	Rat tissues incubated with carotene failed to produce vitamin A, although the whole animal does so in intestinal walls.
175	4/52 4/53	$3,000 3,000	Effects of reducing diets on body composition, physiological function and cholesterol metabolism in the obese.	University of Minnesota	Ancel Keys Henry L. Taylor	J. T. Anderson F. Fidanza	Density of body fat was studied in 8 mammals including man. No general conclusions are yet possible.
183	7/52 6/53	$4,630 4,000	Effects of changes in small intestinal motility upon absorption of specific nutrients.	Washington University	A. I. Mendeloff	—	The effect of eating and sham feeding on the absorption of vitamin A palmitate in man has thrown light on this neglected area of gastrointestinal physiology.
208	9/54 6/55	$1,000 1,000	Metabolism studies of young college women.	North Texas State College	Florence I. Scoular	A. Nell Davis	Analyses of magnesium, calcium and phosphorus have been made on food and excreta. Suggestion is made that 29.1 cal./inch $\pm10\%$ be used as measure of caloric adequacy of diets for such women.

12. PROTEINS AND AMINO ACIDS

Grant No.	Date and Amount	Subject	Institution	Principal Investigators	Co-Workers	Results Reported
7	10/40 $1,500 9/41 1,500 7/42 1,380	Dietary proteins and regeneration of serum albumin.	Columbia University	A. A. Weech E. Goettsch	J. D. Lyttle W. M. Grim P. Dunbar	The serum albumin regenerating power of the following proteins is in the order named: lactalbumin, beef serum, cow's colostrum, whole egg, cow's milk casein. Prolonged low protein intake impairs liver function and rate of serum albumin regeneration.
29	6/42 $1,380 7/43 3,000	Metabolism of amino acids in protein deficiencies.	Columbia University	E. Goettsch	J. D. Lyttle W. M. Grim P. Dunbar	Polypeptides injected into human subjects are excreted and lost. Amino acids tagged with isotopic nitrogen are converted rapidly into ammonia. The speed of incorporation into serum proteins is much slower. (Work stopped on account of war conditions.)
43	7/43 $1,420	Study of regeneration of plasma-proteins following blood donations.	New York University	Frank Co Tui	F. C. Bartter A. M. Wright R. B. Holt	3 donors after each of 4 to 12 blood donations recovered full plasma protein and hematocrit within 48 hours. Reinfusion of red cells into frequent donors is recommended.
68	3/46 $5,000 6/47 2,000	Biosynthesis of amino acids and vitamins by mutant strains of neurospora and E. coli.	Yale University	E. L. Tatum	—	The metabolism of proline, glutamic acid, methionine, cystine, phenylalanine, tyrosine and ergosterol were compared in various organisms.
78	5/47 $6,260	Evaluation of six food proteins on human subjects.	University of Rochester	John R. Murlin	—	Biological values obtained by human feeding ranged from 42 for wheat gluten to 94 for whole egg. The percentage of creatinine in the urine during the closing days of experiment correlated well with biological value. (See #149, page 107.)
87	6/47 $2,400 6/48 2,500 4/49 3,000 6/50 3,000 5/51 3,000 3/53 1,100 6/53 3,000	a) Tryptophan, niacin, pyridoxine and fat. b) Essential amino acid balance.	Alabama Polytechnic Institute	W. D. Salmon H. E. Sauberlich	—	A systematic study was made of the trypto-phan-niacin requirements of the rat; the dependence of tryptophan and methionine requirements on total intake of protein or amino acids; amino acid imbalances, etc.

No.	Date	Amount	Collaborators	Investigator	Institution	Project	Findings
106	7/48 4/49 4/50	$3,500 3,810 3,500	—	Jakob A. Stekol	Lankenau Hospital Research Institute, Philadelphia	Cystathionine, homolanthionine and lanthionine.	In rats synthesis of the labile methyl group from formic acid occurs. Either the L- or D-form of homolanthionine is active for growth in the rat; the meso form is not. Cystathionine is formed from homocysteine and serine.
128	7/49 10/51	$3,000 3,000	—	Barnett Sure	University of Arkansas	Vitamin B_{12} enrichment of vegetable proteins.	Supplementation of cereals with B_{12} or lysine enhanced the growth of rats substantially.
135	3/50 6/51	$3,700 3,000	—	Ernest Geiger	University of Southern California	Mechanism of protein synthesis investigated with the method of delayed supplementation.	Sugar may be used to make non-essential amino acids. Utilization of amino acids is better if absorption is fairly slow. The stomach empties out deficient proteins faster than complete ones. Non-essential amino acids do not have to be fed simultaneously with essentials for good utilization. Testosterone does not affect rate of protein depletion or repletion in rats.
149	5/51	$4,470	—	John R. Murlin	University of Rochester	Creatinine nitrogen percentage as check on biological value of proteins.	Experiments with dogs indicate that the creatinine in the urine is a fairly accurate index of the biological value of the protein ingested. (See #78, page 106.)
159	10/51	$3,700	M. Abdulnabi	John G. Bieri	University of Texas	Protein metabolism in vitamin A deficiency.	Vitamin A deficient rats exhibit few differences from normals in the concentration of amino acids in serum, liver or testes. Threonine was low in deficient livers; phenylalanine and tyrosine were high in deficient testes.
161	12/52 10/53 5/54 9/54 1/55 5/55 11/55	$ 600 188 2,500 230 24 2,581 241	—	A. Sreenivasan	University of Bombay	Utilization of amino acids from low quality proteins as influenced by the B group of vitamins with special reference to folic acid and vitamin B_{12}.	Supplementation with B vitamins of a rice-legume dietary did not result in better performance of rats. Split feeding of protein and non-protein portions reduced nitrogen retention. This disturbance was largely offset by increased B vitamins intake. Studies have been started on porphyrin formation as affected by folic acid and B_{12} additions.
162	7/52	$4,000	P. Fatterpaker G. Litwack L. Chen	J. N. Williams, Jr.	University of Wisconsin	Interrelationships of the B vitamins and dietary proteins.	Correlation was observed between xanthine oxidase activity and growth of animals. B_{12} sometimes enhances xanthine oxidase activity but not consistently.

Grant No.	Date and Amount		Subject	Institution	Principal Investigators	Co-Workers	Results Reported
169	5/52 9/53	$3,000 1,800	Mechanism of plasma protein turnover.	University of Chicago	H. S. Anker	—	Rates of decay of isotopically labeled amino acids failed to give a definitive measure of the protein turnover.
170	4/52	$5,000	Rate of synthesis of proteins by use of labeled arginine and glutamic acid.	Johns Hopkins University	Frederick W. Barnes, Jr.	—	Attempts to measure rates of regeneration of proteins following tissue damage were not highly successful, but many radio-chemical techniques for further use were developed.
180	4/52 6/53	$1,250 1,250	Incorporation of radio-lysine into protein.	California Institute of Technology	Richard S. Schweet	J. T. Holden P. Lowy	Lysine is converted to its alpha keto acid which cyclizes to delta-dehydropipecolic acid. Another lysine metabolite is N-acetyl-alpha-hydroxy-epsilon-aminocaproic acid. An enzyme which incorporates lysine into protein was partially purified.
182	5/52	$2,272	Metabolism of amino acids with radioactive carbon.	University of Illinois	George Wolf	Pei Hzing Lin Wu	Urocanic acid was isolated from rat urine, indicating it is an intermediate in the conversion of histidine to glutamic acid.
198	10/53 6/54 11/54 2/55 6/55 11/55 5/56	$ 5,000 5,000 5,000 101 4,899 5,000 33	Protein malnutrition and kwashiorkor.	University of Cape Town, South Africa	John F. Brock	J. D. L. Hansen E. E. Howe P. J. Pretorius G. A. Davel R. G. Henrickse	Kwashiorkor responds favorably to 11 amino acids including the 8 essential ones. (See text, pages 81 and 83.)
198-A	6/56	$7,842	Biochemical studies of kwashiorkor.	University of Cape Town, South Africa	John F. Brock	H. E. Schendel	So far further training in microchemical methods has been secured by Dr. Schendel at Washington University, St. Louis. These methods will be applied to kwashiorkor cases in South Africa.
213	1/55 12/55	$4,000 5,000	Biosynthesis of aromatic compounds from labeled carbohydrates.	Columbia University	David B. Sprinson	—	The biosynthesis of shikimic acid, a precursor of the benzene ring of aromatic amino acids, has been defined in 3 successive steps using labeled glucose with cell free extracts of E. coli.
218	6/55	$1,200	Phospholipid-bound amino acids.	California Institute of Technology	Herschel K. Mitchell	—	Work in progress.

No.	Date	Amount	Project	Institution	Investigators	Notes
220	12/55	$4,595	Nutritional and biochemical investigations of sulphur containing amino acids.	Vanderbilt University	H. Vasken Aposhian	—	Work in progress.

13. REQUIREMENTS FOR VITAMINS

No.	Date	Amount	Project	Institution	Investigators	Notes
8	9/40 10/41	$1,250 1,330	Estimation of human requirement for B_1.	Mt. Sinai Hospital, New York City	Herbert Pollack, Max Ellenberger, Henry Dolger	—	In dietary deficiency of B_1, thiamine excretion is promptly reduced, but excretion of pyrimidine is maintained longer. If thiamine is low and pyrimidine high, temporary deprivation of B_1 is indicated; if both are low, prolonged deprivation is indicated.
9	11/40 10/41	$2,400 3,700	B_1 requirements of women during pregnancy and lactation.	Massachusetts Institute of Technology	Robert S. Harris, Edward Josephson	—	The thiamine requirement in early pregnancy is normal but rises to 6-8 times normal in the 6th to 9th month and continues in the post-partum period whether lactating or not. Amer. Jour. of Obstetrics and Gynecology 46, 385 (1943).
16	6/41 4/42	$3,600 3,600	Riboflavin in American foods.	Columbia University	Henry C. Sherman	—	Average riboflavin intake is estimated at 2.3 mgs. per day as compared with 2.2 mgs., the weighted Daily Recommended Allowance of N.R.C.
46	11/42 10/43	$3,000 3,500	Human requirements for B vitamins.	Johns Hopkins University	L. Emmett Holt	—	Synthesis of thiamine by intestinal bacteria in humans is significant. It may be inhibited by sulfonamide drugs. Minor clinical symptoms of B deficiencies need to be supported by biochemistry of blood and urine.
48	3/44	$2,000	Riboflavin requirement of the adult.	University of Chicago	Lydia J. Roberts	—	In young women on diets controlled 4-6 months with an intake of 0.5 mg. of riboflavin per 1,000 calories, tissue stores were maintained; they were not on lower intakes. For thiamine the critical intake was about the same—0.51 mg. per 1,000 calories. 1 mg. of each per 1,000 calories is a minimum safe level.
130	9/49	$3,200	Thiamine requirement for human lactation.	New York University	L. Emmett Holt	—	Some breast-fed babies do not receive adequate thiamine. Samples of pooled breast milk varied considerably in thiamine content.

14. SURVEYS OF NUTRITIONAL STATUS

Grant No.	Date and Amount	Subject	Institution	Principal Investigators	Co-Workers	Results Reported
163-A	6, 7 and 10/54 $14,948	Nutritional status of Formosan civilians.	American Bureau for Medical Aid to China	Norman Jolliffe	—	About 2,000 sixth grade school children and 200 adults were examined clinically, 15 young Chinese physicians participating and receiving instruction in diagnosis. Confirmation by biochemical assays was achieved in 20 per cent of the subjects. Riboflavin deficiency is very high, vitamin A deficiency moderately severe; thiamine levels are marginal. (See text, page 38.)
184	6/52 $3,624 7/52 1,060 12/52 1,873 9/54 4,896 5/55 1,533 12/55 3,300	Survey of nutritional deficiencies in Vellore.	Christian Medical College Hospital Vellore, India	John S. Carman	—	Due to lack of trained staff and remoteness from facilities for repair of equipment, little progress has been made except in vitamin C determinations.
193	3/53 $1,769	Completion of Central American dietary surveys of 1950 and initiation of dietary surveys in Cuba.	Pan American Sanitary Bureau	Nevin S. Scrimshaw	Emma Reh	A dietary survey of one town in Cuba was carried out, several Cuban women receiving training in the techniques.
217	5/54 $4,000	Nutritional status of Chinese Nationalist troops.	—	Herbert Pollack	—	A preliminary tour of inspection was made, and the U. S. Defense Department took up the responsibility.
223	1956 $19,607	Nutritional status of Cuban people.	Fundacion de Investigaciones Medicas	Norman Jolliffe	Hady Lopez Margarita Cimadevilla T. B. Van Itallie Kenneth H. Shull Catalina Durruthy Edelmira Fernandez Flavio Galban Robert S. Harris	Clinical examination of about 2,200 Cuban children of 11 to 13 years was conducted with the aid of 17 young Cuban physicians who thus received instruction. Biochemical assays of blood and urine on 20 per cent of the subjects is now in progress. (See text, page 38.)

15. TRAINING PROGRAMS

Grant No.	Date and Amount	Subject	Institution	Principal Investigators	Co-Workers	Results Reported
1	4/40 $3,500 10/42 8,000 4/43 5,000 10/43 8,000 4/44 5,000	Combatting nutritional diseases in the South.	University of Texas later University of Cincinnati	Tom D. Spies	J. K. Cline R. E. Eakin Gordon Morey Martha Bieler Margaret Collwell	1729 consecutive cases of pellagra were successfully treated. Studies were undertaken on the quantitative occurrence of pantothenic acid and riboflavin in human blood and tissues. Search for an antianemic factor in foods got under way. (See text, page 25.)

No.	Date	Amount	Purpose	Institution	Grantee		Remarks
62	5/46 12/47 12/48 8/50 5/52 6/53 10/54 10/55	$5,000 10,500 10,500 10,500 10,500 10,500 7,000 7,000	a) Teaching center work at Birmingham. b) Fellowships in the field of medical nutrition.	Nutrition Clinic, Hillman Hospital, Birmingham	Tom D. Spies	—	Aid or fellowships was provided for the following: Juan Angulo, Tomas Aramburu, R. O. Brandenburg, Catherine Curry, Samuel Dreizen, Sam Kartus, Vicente Lequanoa, Ruben Lopez-Toca, A. Menendez, F. Milanes, George S. Parker, Alfredo Reboredo, Marta Rojas, D. J. Siberman, R. M. Snodgrass, R. E. Stone, Carl F. Vilter (See text, page 25.)
81	3/47	$400	Tour of research on plant physiology in U.S.	Hebrew University, Jerusalem	M. Evenari	—	Report rendered to Committee at conclusion of travel.
110	10/48 4/49 6/50 5/51	$7,000 7,000 7,000 4,500	Program for fellowships in enzyme chemistry.	University of Wisconsin	David E. Green	—	Frank Huennekens: Transformation of oxidases. Ephraim Kaplan: Acetoacetate from pyruvate. Jack Still: Extension of Rockefeller grant. Osamu Hayaishi: DPN-cytochrome reductase. Nirmal Sarkar: Glycine from serine and sarcosine. Priscilla Hele: Non-participation of inorganic phosphate in dehydrogenation via cyclophorase system. C. V. Ramakrishnan: Succinyl-CoA deacylase and acetyl-CoA from acetate and ATP.
176	4/52 6/53 9/54 6/55	$4,123 4,120 4,556 3,910	Nutritional problems related to the diets of South India.	Women's Christian College, Chetput, Madras, India	Dorothy Pearson F. Theophilus R. Arulanantham		Training of students in nutrition is progressing through conduct of modest research projects on Indian diets.
219	6/55	$5,000	Fellowship for Dr. Huang of National Taiwan University, Formosa.	American Bureau for Medical Aid to China	Po-chao Huang	—	Currently studying with Dr. Grace Goldsmith at Tulane University.
225	4/56	$700	Travel grant for study at INCAP.	University of Pennsylvania	Roger Allen Feldman Alan Balsam	—	Travel expenses to Guatemala were furnished for a summer's study of nutritional diseases and their treatment.
ST*	2/56	$258	Expenses for trip from New York to Cuba and return by Dr. Chandrapananda, government nutrition specialist, Bangkok, Thailand.	—	Amara Chandrapananda		Obtained experience in clinical nutrition survey work.
ST	7/52	$3,000	Fellowship for Miss Fatterpaker of the University of Bombay, India.	—	Prema Fatterpaker	—	One year of study at the University of Wisconsin.

* Special Training Grant (ST).

15. TRAINING PROGRAMS (continued)

Grant No.	Date and Amount	Subject	Institution	Principal Investigators	Co-Workers	Results Reported
ST	7/54 $800 9/54 500 2/55 250	Tuition for Miss Manalo of the Institute of Nutrition, Manila, Philippines.		Josefina D. Manalo	—	Studied with Dr. W. A. Krehl, Yale University.
ST	7/55 $1,750	Fellowship for Miss Mendiola of the Manila Health Department, Philippines.		Leticia R. Mendiola	—	Currently studying with Dr. Grace Goldsmith, Tulane University.
ST	12/54 $108 4/55 110	Tuition for Miss Philips of the General Hospital, Colombo, Ceylon.		Hilmi Philips	—	Studied institutional management and food accounting at Columbia University.
ST	11/52 $600	Travel expenses within the U.S. for Dr. A. Sreenivasan of the University of Bombay, India.		A. Sreenivasan	—	Visited several research centers to obtain information pertinent to his research.
ST	4/52 $100 6/52 242	Travel expenses within the U.S. for Dr. Waterlow, University College of the West Indies, Jamaica.		John Waterlow	—	Visited several research centers to receive training in enzymatic methods.
ST	2/53 $1,800	Retainer for Dr. Yenermen of the University of Istanbul.		Munevver Yenermen	—	Studied composition of insulin at National Institute of Health, Bethesda, Maryland.

16. UNCLASSIFIED

Grant No.	Date and Amount	Subject	Institution	Principal Investigators	Co-Workers	Results Reported
13	4/41 $3,000 7/42 3,000 7/43 3,000	Metabolism of carcinogenic agents as affected by dietary constituents.	Memorial Hospital, N. Y.	C. P. Rhoads	Seymour Lieberman	Extensive observations on the metabolism of steroids in normal and cancerous subjects.
14	5/41 $1,000	Gift of vitamins for Chinese orphans.	American Bureau for Medical Aid to China	Donald D. Van Slyke	—	——
40	5/43 $3,000	Pyrimidine biosynthesis.	Stanford University	H. K. Mitchell G. W. Beadle	E. L. Tatum N. H. Horowitz D. M. Bonner	Asexual spores of Neurospora crassa on treatment with X-rays or ultraviolet gave rise to 253 clear biochemical mutants. Those deficient in pyrimidine synthesis were chosen for special study.
54	6/44 $4,640 8/45 3,845 3/47 3,000 6/48 1,750 3/53 900	High niacin corn.	Columbia University	Ray F. Dawson	F. D. Richey	By selective breeding the niacin content was increased 5 fold in 5 years. The microbiological method of niacin assay has been refined. The development of a useful high niacin strain is possible but will require many years. (See text, page 29.)

No.	Date	Amount	Project	Institution	Investigator	Others	Notes
56	5/45	$1,500	Relationship of bacterial flora to intestinal function.	Western Reserve University	Victor C. Myers	—	Resection of colon and caecum transfers bacterial activity to small intestine. Penicillin, unlike sulfonamides, does not sufficiently inhibit intestinal synthesis to produce deficiency symptoms.
65	3/47	$2,085	Biochemistry and biophysics of calcification and ossification, and of decalcification.	University of Chicago	Franklin C. McLean	Jerome Waldman	The "local factor" in calcification is not enzymatic. Further work was abandoned for lack of personnel.
73	7/47 1/51 1/52	$4,400 1,500 1,500	Bacillin and antibacillin.	The University of Texas	Jackson W. Foster	—	Cow's blood generally is a rich source of antibacillin but is sometimes deficient. Improvements in the preparation and preservation of bacillin have been made. An exploration of numerous chemical substances and various micro-organisms for antibacillin activity was only partly successful. Inhibition of many antibiotics by natural substances was encountered.
96	1/48 1/49 10/49 10/51	$10,000 10,000 10,000 10,420	Hormone and vitamin metabolism in psychosis.	The Worcester Foundation for Experimental Biology	Hudson Hoagland Gregory Pincus	—	Studies included responses of schizophrenics to ACTH, adrenal extracts, and specific steroids including cortisone. There were promising indications but no practical therapy resulted.
105	6/48 4/49	$3,000 3,000	Incidence of caries in the cotton rat in relation to the composition of teeth, bones, blood and diet.	Jewish Hospital of Brooklyn	Albert E. Sobel	Albert Hanok Howard Kirchner I. Fankuchen Sidney Nobel	The normal predominant mineral in teeth is apatite. When the molar calcium phosphate ratio in the diet is 1.5 or less, beta calcium phosphate replaces apatite.
123	5/49 6/50 6/51	$27,275 21,163 20,975	Metabolic inhibitors as chemotherapeutic agents in the control of cancer and viral invasions.	Amherst College	George W. Kidder	V. C. Dewey R. E. Parks	Guanazalo (an analog of guanine) was found to inhibit the growth of several, but not all, mouse tumors. The general idea of a specific antimetabolite for cancer cells is being pursued by numerous workers. (See text, page 28.)
124	5/49 6/50 6/51	$5,975 5,400 4,000	Chemotherapeutic studies on cancer in mice.	University of Massachusetts	Gilbert L. Woodside	G. W. Kidder	Collaboration with Dr. Kidder on Grant #123.
140	9/50	$4,000	Enzymatic synthesis of nucleic acid units in cell components and bacteriophages.	University Institute for Cell Physiology Copenhagen, Denmark	Herman M. Kalckar	—	Funds were used for purchase of a vacuum ultracentrifuge.

16. UNCLASSIFIED (continued)

Grant No.	Date and Amount	Subject	Institution	Principal Investigators	Co-Workers	Results Reported
143	9/50 $5,000 6/51 5,240 7/52 5,240 7/53 5,240 6/54 5,240 6/55 5,000	a) Effects of maternal nutrition on the young. b) Nutrition of rats with compounds of known structure.	University of Minnesota	M. O. Schultze	L. E. Hallanger J. W. Laakso J. E. Gander P. A. Hedin I. E. Liener R. L. Glass	Four successive generations of rats were fed protein-free diets, nitrogen being supplied by 10 amino acids and ammonium citrate. The young survived but growth was slow. Lactation induced a 20% loss of weight in the mothers, and fatty livers developed. Rat milk is low in sugar, high in fat and protein. Studies are continuing on ability of diets containing only known compounds to support successive generations of rats.
145	11/50 $4,600 10/51 4,350 12/52 4,600 2/54 4,700 1/55 4,700	Feeding antibiotics to domestic fowl.	Texas Agricultural Experiment Station	J. R. Couch L. L. Gee	——	The effect of antibiotics is to modify the intestinal flora which is sometimes favorable, sometimes unfavorable to the host.
150	5/51 $5,000 7/52 4,000	Synthesis and biological role of glucuronic acid-1-phosphate.	Vanderbilt University	Oscar Touster	——	Numerous avenues have been explored to learn the role of glucuronides. L-xylulose, excreted by persons affected with pentosuria, is also present in small amounts in normal persons. This pentose is presumed to have a normal physiological rcle.
154	7/51 $5,000	Requirements of swine for normal reproduction.	State College of Washington	M. E. Ensminger Burch H. Schneider	——	The experiment had to be discontinued because of an epidemic of brucellosis. (See grant #189.)
157	8/51 $539	Purchase of books.	Institute of Nutrition, Manila, Philippines	——	——	——
158	10/51 $3,000	Nutritional requirements of crustaceans.	University of Texas	Ernest Beerstecher, Jr.	——	Partial definition of the requirements of Oniscus asellus (pill bug) and Daphnia pulex (water flea) has been achieved.
179	3/53 $1,600	For purchase of quartz spectrophotometer.	Aarhus University Psychiatric Institute Risskov, Denmark	Mogens Schou	——	——
189	12/52 $3,000	Requirements of swine for normal growth and reproduction.	The State College of Washington	M. E. Ensminger Burch H. Schneider	——	Some data have been collected on the energy requirements at 20 and 30% protein. The experiments are still in progress. (See grant #154.)

No.	Date	Amount	Purpose	Institution	Investigator(s)	Remarks
194	6/53	$484	Purchase of Densichron densitometer for general use.	Instituto de Nutricao Rio de Janeiro, Brazil	Ottilio Guernelli	—
195	12/53 12/55 1/56 2/56 3/56	$3,340 16 1,175 3,159 5	Metabolic patterns of rats differing genetically in their voluntary alcohol intake.	University of Chile Santiago, Chile	Jorge Mardones Natividad Segovia Riquelme	To prepare for further study, Dr. Natividad Segovia Riquelme took one year's training at Harvard with Drs. Stare and Hegsted in radio-carbon techniques. No significant metabolic feature has been correlated with appetite for alcohol thus far.
196	1/54	$1,090	For purchase of Farrand photo-electric fluorometer.	University of Oxford Oxford, England	H. M. Sinclair	—
202	6/54	$3,007	For purchase of Beckman photo-electric quartz spectrophotometer and accessories.	Central Food Technological Research Institute, Mysore, India	V. Subrahmanyan	—
203	5/54	$1,800	Investigation of poisonous fishes and their relationship to protein food sources.	College of Medical Evangelists	Bruce W. Halstead	Toxic properties are not universal within a species, and the pattern is very erratic. 4,800 pounds of a large variety of fishes and organisms on which they feed have been collected and are being analyzed for toxic properties.
S*	12/55	$500	Toward publication of monograph, "The Effect of Mothers' Diets on the Intelligence of Offspring."	Columbia University	Ruth F. Harrell Ella Woodyard Arthur I. Gates	—
S	6/50	$200	To help defray deficit of the Nutrition Division.	Health Council of Greater New York	—	—
S	5/54	$1,200	Gift of laboratory equipment.	National Defense Medical Center, Taiwan	—	—
S	7/55 11/55 3/56	$1,591 89 71	To act as consultant to all Indian and Pakistan projects.	University of Bombay Bombay, India	A. Sreenivasan	Visits have been made semi-annually to Madras, Vellore and Lahore.
S	12/51	$900	For purchase of motion picture projector.	Stewart School and Science College, Cuttack, India	—	—

* Special Grant (S).

17. VITAMINS, GENERAL

No.	Date	Amount	Purpose	Institution	Investigator(s)	Remarks
2	4/40 6/41	$1,250 5,000	Muscular dystrophy in rabbits as affected by alpha-tocopherol.	Johns Hopkins University	E. V. McCollum C. G. Mackenzie Julia B. Mackenzie Milton D. Levine Harold Blumberg	Tocopherol is potent orally at 20 mg., but inactive parenterally.

17. VITAMINS, GENERAL (continued)

Grant No.	Date and Amount	Subject	Institution	Principal Investigators	Co-Workers	Results Reported
36	1943 $3,000	Thiamine and riboflavin inter-relationship in metabolism.	University of Arkansas	Barnett Sure	Z. W. Ford	Thiamine deficiency produces losses of riboflavin in urine, hence lowers riboflavin in tissues.
41	7/43 $3,500	Growth factor requirements and production of vitamins by yeasts, molds and bacteria.	Yale University	Paul R. Burkholder	—	Growth factor requirements have been determined for 163 strains of yeasts. Large numbers of organisms have been collected and are being tested for production of riboflavin and other B vitamins.
44	3/45 $600	Choline intake and choline storage in body tissues.	Texas A. & M. College	P. B. Pearson	—	1, 2 or 4% choline in the diet progressively reduced the growth rate of chickens. Rats and rabbits are more sensitive to excess choline. 2% choline in the diet increased choline in the liver by 70%; 4% increased it by 117%.
58	10/45 $3,000 11/46 2,800 10/47 3,000	Oxybiotin.	University of Pittsburgh	Klaus Hofmann A. E. Axelrod	—	Oxybiotin has biotin activity in micro-organisms, not due to its conversion to biotin. Oxybiotin can replace biotin for the chick, and the resulting storage of "biotin activity" in tissues is in a water-insoluble form.
61	12/45 $3,000 12/46 3,000	Role of folic acid in cancer.	Mt. Sinai Hospital, New York City	John C. Keresztesy	—	Folic acid caused regression in certain tumors in mice. Both in cancerous mice and humans there was rapid conversion of pteropterin to glutamate forms. Folic acid content of tumor tissues was not revealing.
70	5/46 $4,940	Biochemistry of Lactobacillus casei factor.	University of Arkansas	John R. Totter	Edith S. Sims Ruth Steinkamp Carroll F. Shukers Paul L. Day	Pteroylglutamic acid modifies porphyrin formation probably by its effect on xanthine oxidase. Conversion of glycine to serine is governed by PGA concentration.
75	10/46 $1,000 10/47 1,000	Pantothenic acid in the nitrogen metabolism of bacteria.	University of Iowa	J. R. Porter	—	The role of pantothenic acid in the utilization of amino acids was explored with micro-organisms. Various hints of coenzyme A activity were encountered.
103	3/48 $2,500 1/49 2,500	Pantothenic acid and niacin needs of the sow during gestation and lactation.	State College of Washington	M. E. Ensminger	E. E. Goodwin B. H. Schneider	All experimental animals were destroyed by fire, and the experiments must be repeated.

No.	Dates	Amounts	Title	Institution	Investigator	Co-workers	Description
122	4/49 4/50 6/51	$1,900 3,300 3,530	Stability of thiamine.	Fordham University	Douglas J. Hennessy	E. Kupstas R. J. Moshy E. J. DiBella	Studies on thiamine included: inactivation by clam tissue; reversible oxidation in animal tissue; stabilization by sulfhydryl compounds; free radical behavior of thiamine disulfide; action of borohydrides on thiamine. Mixed disulfides of thiamine, two forms of S-methyl thiamine and 2-methylthiazolium analogs were prepared.
127	6/49	$3,000	Folic acid in formate metabolism.	University of Wisconsin	Henry A. Lardy	G. W. E. Plaut J. Betheil Katherine Armstrong Gladys Feldott	Rats made folic acid deficient by a purified diet and succinyl sulfathiazole were given C^{14} tagged formate. Deficient rats fixed only one-tenth as much C^{14} in liver and one-third as much in viscera as normals. Kidneys from rats deficient in B_6 showed only one-third as much D-amino oxidase as normals.
160	10/51 12/52 9/53 1/55 12/55	$1,100 1,000 551 752 1,349	Nutritional significance of folinic acid.	Baylor University	T. J. Bond	—	The conversion of folic acid to folinic acid is enzymatic, and the enzyme systems involved are under study.
171	4/52	$3,600	Interrelated biochemical functions of folic acid and vitamin B_{12}.	Cornell University	Louise J. Daniel	J. R. Christensen N. I. Mondy D. R. Strength	Folic acid appears to affect choline oxidation indirectly by its effect on synthesis of purine. B_{12} apparently does not affect choline oxidation.
174	5/52	$6,000	Multiple congenital abnormalities produced by maternal pteroyl-glutamic acid deficiency.	University of California	Herbert M. Evans	I. W. Monie C. W. Asling H. V. Wright	A 2-day period of deficiency immediately after implantation results in fetal death. Congenital abnormalities of bones, eyes, cardiac blood vessels, etc. were found.
187	7/52 6/53	$3,100 3,000	Effect of Vitamin B_{12} on the level of ergothioneine, glutathione and total sulfhydryl groups in rat erythrocytes.	College of Medical Evangelists	U. D. Register	—	Vitamin B_{12} tends to concentrate in kidneys. It promotes pyruvate oxidation and maintains the level of sulphydryl groups in blood. A high protein diet aggravates B_{12} deficiency; high carbohydrate does so to a lesser extent; high fat has a sparing effect.
191	3/53 9/54	$3,000 2,150	Riboflavin in storage of vitamin B_{12}.	Adelphi College	Lillian N. Ellis	—	While better growth was obtained with levels of riboflavin or folic acid above the subminimal, no increase in storage of B_{12} was noted.
216	5/55 3/56	$2,250 2,614	Relationship of pantothenic acid to adrenocortical hormone secretion.	Washington University School of Medicine	Albert B. Eisenstein	—	Synthesis of steroid hormones in rat adrenals is reduced by pantothenic acid deficiency. Studies still in progress.

Williams-Waterman Fund
Grantees and Co-workers

Following each name is one or more pairs of numbers. The first number, italicized, refers to the category in the preceding list of grants; the second number indicates the grant within that category. An asterisk signifies "Principal Investigator"; no asterisk means "Co-worker."

Abdulnabi, M. *12*, 159
Ahmad, Bashir *4*, 186*
Ahrens, E. H. *7*, 221*
Albert, K. *10*, 60
Ames, B. N. *2*, 64
Anderson, D. G. *6*, 141
Anderson, J. T. *11*, 175
Angulo, Juan *15*, 62
Anker, H. S. *12*, 169*
Aposhian, H. Vasken *12*, 220*
Appleby, D. C. *7*, 125
Aramburu, Tomas *15*, 62
Armstrong, Katherine *17*, 127
Arroyave, Guillermo *4*, 200
Arulanantham, R. *4*, 178; *15*, 176
Asling, C. W. *17*, 174
Atwater, Reginald T. *5*, 165*
Axelrod, A. E. *17*, 58*
Aykroyd, W. R. *3*, 164*

Babcock, S. H. *9*, 4*
Baddiley, J. *6*, 141
Baker, B. R. *9*, 4
Bakwin, Harry *8*, 35*
Balsam, Alan *15*, 225*
Barnes, Frederick W., Jr. *12*, 170*
Bartter, F. C. *12*, 43
Beadle, G. W. *2*, 64*; *16*, 40*
Beams, A. J. *8*, 34
Beerstecher, Jr., Ernest *16*, 158*
Bell, John P. *3*, 95
Bernheim, Frederick *7*, 118*
Betheil, J. *17*, 127
Bieler, Martha *15*, 1
Bieri, John G. *12*, 159*
Blanchard, M. *6*, 50
Blodgett, Hugh C. *10*, 31*
Blumberg, Harold *17*, 2
Bond, T. J. *17*, 160*
Bonner, David M. *2*, 77*; *16*, 40
Bonner, James *6*, 10
Borcham, I. *8*, 42
Borek, Ernest *10*, 60

Borsook, Henry *1*, 3*; *4*, 37*
Boyd, R. B. *6*, 148
Braham, J. Edgar *4*, 200
Brandenburg, R. O. *15*, 62
Brock, John F. *12*, 198*; *12*, 198-A*
Buchman, Edwin R. *1*, 3; *6*, 10*
Bueding, Ernest *8*, 12; *8*, 38; *11*, 92*
Burch, Helen B. *3*, 109*; *6*, 190*
Burkholder, Paul R. *17*, 41*
Burton, R. M. *6*, 147

Caldwell, Mary L. *6*, 121*
Cantoni, G. L. *6*, 141*
Carleen, M. H. *1*, 11
Carman, John S. *14*, 184*
Carpenter, D. C. *9*, 79*
Carrasco, Eufronio O. *3*, 84*
Chandrapananda, Amara *15*, ST*
Cheldelin, Vernon H. *1*, 20; *9*, 47*; *9*, 63*; *6*, 197*
Chen, L. *12*, 162
Chester, Annette *11*, 27
Christensen, J. R. *17*, 171
Chugtai, M. D. *4*, 186
Cimadevilla, Margarita *1*, 185; *14*, 223
Ciotti, M. M. *6*, 147
Claridge, C. A. *6*, 197
Cline, J. K. *15*, 1; *9*, 74*
Clinton, M. *1*, 11
Coburn, A. F. *8*, 22*
Cohen, Jonathan *8*, 97
Collwell, Margaret *15*, 1
Colowick, Sidney P. *6*, 147*
Coon, M. J. *6*, 151
Co Tui, Frank *8*, 42*; *12*, 43*
Couch, J. R. *16*, 145*
Craig, John *8*, 97
Curry, Catherine *15*, 62

Daniel, Louise J. *17*, 171*
Darby, William J. *3*, 172*

Davel, G. A. *12*, 198
Davis, A. Nell *11*, 208
Davis, P. O. *3*, 95*; *3*, 116*
Dawson, Ray F. *16*, 54*
Day, Paul L. *17*, 70
Del Campillo, A. *6*, 151
Dewey, Virginia C. *2*, 94; *2*, 117; *16*, 123
DiBella, E. J. *17*, 122
Dickins, Dorothy *3*, 173*
Dolger, Henry *13*, 8*
Dove, Margaret A. *3*, 53
Dove, Robert *3*, 53*
Dreizen, Samuel *15*, 62
Drell, William *2*, 64
Dunbar, P. *12*, 7; *12*, 29
Dunn, M. S. *1*, 138*
Durruthy, Catalina *14*, 223

Eakin, R. E. *1*, 20; *15*, 1
Earnest, C. B. *3*, 152
Eisenstein, Albert B. *17*, 216*
Ellenberger, Max *13*, 8*
Ellis, Lillian N. *17*, 191*
Ensminger, M. E. *17*, 103*; *16*, 154*; *16*, 189*
Evans, Herbert M. *17*, 174*
Evenari, M. *15*, 81*

Fankuchen, I. *16*, 105
Farber, S. *8*, 97
Fatterpaker, Prema *12*, 162; *15*, ST
Fazekas, Y. F. *8*, 12
Fearing, R. B. *1*, 93
Feldman, Roger Allen, *15*, 225*
Feldott, Gladys *17*, 127
Fernandez, Edelmira *1*, 185; *14*, 223
Ferrebee, J. W. *1*, 11*
Fidanza, F. *11*, 175
Ford, Z. W. *17*, 36
Forrest, H. S. *2*, 64
Foster, Jackson W. *16*, 73*
Fox, Sidney W. *1*, 93*; *6*, 90*
Free, A. H. *8*, 34

Freed, V. H. *6*, 80
Freeston, Sir Brian *1*, 207*
Friend, Shirley *3*, 192

Galban, Flavio *14*, 223
Gander, J. E. *16*, 143
Gates, Arthur I. *10*, 15; *10*, 59*
Gee, L. L. *16*, 145*
Geiger, A. *10*, 91*
Geiger, Ernest *12*, 135*
Geller, Edward *1*, 138
Glass, R. L. *16*, 143
Glusman, Murray *8*, 82*
Goettsch, E. *12*, 7; *12*, 29*
Goldfarb, W. *8*, 12
Goldsmith, Grace A. *3*, 53*; *3*, 108*, *8*, 57*
Goodhart, R. *8*, 12
Goodwin, E. E. *17*, 103
Gourevitch, A. *7*, 125
Green, David E. *6*, 50*; *8*, 22*; *15*, 110*
Green, Harry *6*, 144
Grim, W. M. *12*, 7; *12*, 29
Guernelli, Ottilio *16*, 194*

Haag, J. R. *6*, 80*
Hagdahl, James H. *1*, 86
Hallanger, L. E. *16*, 143
Halstead, Bruce W. *16*, 203*
Handler, Philip *2*, 112
Hanok, Albert *16*, 105
Hansen, J. D. L. *12*, 198
Harlan, Harriet A. *3*, 85
Harrell, Ruth *10*, 15*; *10*, 59*
Harris, Daniel L. *2*, 226*
Harris, Robert S. *1*, 185*; *7*, 139*; *13*, 9*; *14*, 223
Haskins, F. A. *2*, 64
Hatcher, J. B. *1*, 3
Hauge, Jens G. *6*, 197
Hayaishi, Osamu *15*, 110
Hedin, P. A. *16*, 143
Heegaard, Erik *6*, 10
Hegsted, D. M. *11*, 98*
Heimberg, Murray *2*, 112
Hele, Priscilla *15*, 110
Hennessy, Douglas J. *17*, 122*
Henrickse, R. G. *12*, 198
Herbst, Edward J. *9*, 72; *9*, 146*
Herrlich, H. *8*, 12
Himwich, H. E. *8*, 12; *11*, 27*; *11*, 49*
Hoagland, Hudson *16*, 96*
Hoch, P. A. *10*, 60
Hofmann, Klaus *17*, 58*
Holden, J. T. *12*, 180
Holman, Ralph T. *1*, 86*
Holt, L. Emmett, Jr. *1*, 24*; *1*, 30*; *13*, 46*; *13*, 130*
Holt, R. B. *12*, 43
Homburger, Edmund *11*, 27
Hoobler, Icie Macy *5*, 205*
Horlacher, W. R. *1*, 26*
Horowitz, N. H. *6*, 10; *16*, 40
Howe, E. E. *12*, 198
Huang, Po-chao *15*, 219*
Hubbard, D. D. *9*, 146
Huennekens, Frank *15*, 110
Hulse, M. C. *1*, 11
Hunter, Sylvia *2*, 112

Hutner, S. H. *1*, 215*

Jackson, Blanche *10*, 23
Jamieson, G. A. *6*, 141
Jeans, P. C. *8*, 115*
Jerzy Glass, George B. *8*, 227*
Johnson, R. B. *9*, 74
Johnston, Frances A. *3*, 192*
Jolliffe, Norman *4*, 99*; *5*, 83*; *5*, 89*; *8*, 12*; *8*, 38*; *8*, 166*; *14*, 163-A*; *14*, 223
Jones, L. I. *3*, 114*
Josephson, Edward *13*, 9*
Jukes, T. H. *9*, 4*

Kalckar, Herman M. *16*, 140*
Kaplan, Ann *6*, 144
Kaplan, Ephraim *15*, 110
Kaplan, Nathan O. *6*, 147*
Karn, H. W. *10*, 6*
Kartus, Sam *15*, 62
Kearney, Edna B. *6*, 132
Kemmerer, Arthur R. *1*, 69*
Keresztesy, John C. *17*, 61*
Ketron, Katherine C. *1*, 24
Keys, Ancel *5*, 131*; *11*, 175*
Kidder, George W. *2*, 94*; *2*, 117*; *16*, 123*; *16*, 124
Kihara, H. *9*, 72
Kik, M. C. *1*, 26*
King, C. G. *10*, 6*
King, Tsoo E. *6*, 197
Kirchner, Howard *16*, 105
Kirkwood, Samuel *13*, 9
Kleiger, Sarah C. *1*, 5
Knott, Elizabeth M. *1*, 5*
Kornberg, A. *6*, 55; *9*, 47
Krehl, W. A. *2*, 25; *2*, 77
Kupstas, E. *17*, 122

Laakso, J. W. *16*, 143
Lacroix, P. *8*, 97
Landman, O. E. *2*, 77
Langham, W. H. *2*, 64
Lardy, Henry A. *17*, 127*
Lease, E. J. *3*, 33*; *5*, 28*
Leder, Irwin *2*, 112
Lein, Joseph *7*, 125*
Lein, P. S. *7*, 125
Leland, Marita *3*, 192
Leonards, J. R. *8*, 34
Lequanoa, Vicente *15*, 62
Leslie, Ruth *4*, 19*
Levine, Milton D. *17*, 2
Lichstein, Herman C. *6*, 148*
Lieberman, Seymour *16*, 13
Liefer, E. *2*, 64
Liener, I. E. *16*, 143
Linn, Dorothy R. *3*, 85
Litwack, G. *12*, 162
Lopez, Hady *1*, 185; *14*, 223
Lopez-Toca, Ruben *15*, 62
Lowy, P. *12*, 180
Lyman, Carl M. *1*, 111
Lyttle, J. D. *12*, 7; *12*, 29

MacFarlane, Y. *1*, 207
Mackenzie, C. G. *11*, 32; *17*, 2*
Mackenzie, Julia B. *11*, 32; *17*, 2
Maddock, Charlotte *8*, 97

Maddock, Stephen *8*, 97
Magnes, J. *10*, 91*
Mahan, J. R. I. *20*
Manalo, Josefina D. *15*, ST*
Mardones, Jorge *16*, 195*
Mason, Eleanor D. *15*, 176*
May, Charles D. *8*, 88*
McCollum, E. V. *11*, 32*; *17*, 2*
McDevitt, Ellen *3*, 53*
McLean, Franklin C. *16*, 65*
McMillan, Edwin *1*, 3
McQueeney, A. J. *3*, 51
Mehler, Alan *6*, 55
Mendeloff, A. I. *11*, 183*
Mendiola, Leticia R. *15*, ST*
Menendez, A. *15*, 62
Metcoff, J. *3*, 51
Meyerhof, Otto *6*, 144*
Milanes, F. *15*, 62
Miller, Herbert K. *10*, 60
Miller, Max *11*, 92*
Mitchell, Herschel K. *1*, 20; *2*, 64*; *12*, 218*; *16*, 40*
Mondy, N. I. *17*, 171
Monie, I. W. *17*, 174
Morey, Gordon *15*, 1
Mosher, Malcolm *13*, 9
Moshy, R. J. *17*, 122
Most, Rita M. *8*, 38
Mulholland, J. J. *8*, 42
Murlin, John R. *12*, 78*; *12*, 149*
Murray, C. C. *3*, 152*
Murray, Anna Z. *13*, 16
Myers, Victor C. *8*, 34*; *16*, 56*

Najjar, Victor A. *1*, 24
Nason, A. *6*, 147
Navia, Juan *1*, 185
Nelson, Marjorie M. *17*, **174***
Newburgh, R. W. *6*, 197
Niemeyer, Hermann *6*, 199*
Nobel, Sidney *16*, 105
Nocito-Carroll, V. *6*, 50
Noland, John *3*, 152
Nyc, J. F. *2*, 64

Ochoa, Severo *6*, 21*; *6*, 55*; *6*, 151*
Oldewurtel, H. A. *6*, 147
Olivard, Joanne *6*, 212
Olson, Robert E. *8*, 177*
Owades, Phyllis *10*, 60

Parker, George S. *15*, 62
Parks, R. E. *16*, 123
Partridge, C. W. H. *2*, 77
Pascual, Conrado R. *1*, 206*
Patton, Robert A. *10*, 6*; *10*, 104*
Pearson, Dorothy *15*, 176
Pearson, P. B. *1*, 111*; *17*, 44*
Pennington, Derrol *1*, 20
Perlzweig, W. A. *2*, 112*
Peters, F. *1*, 207
Petty, C. S. *8*, 97
Philips, Hilmi *15*, ST*
Pincus, Gregory *16*, 96*
Plaut, Gerhard W. E. *6*, 222*; *17*, 127

Pollack, Herbert *13*, 8*; *14*, 217*
Porter, J. R. *17*, 75*
Post, Joseph *8*, 133*
Prescott, Blanche A. *10*, 60
Pretorius, P. J. *12*, 198
Price, J. C. *10*, 60
Puglisi, T. A. *7*, 125
Pullman, M. E. *6*, 147

Ramakrishnan, C. V. *15*, 110
Ratner, Sarah *6*, 50; *6*, 101*
Reboredo, Alfredo *15*, 62
Register, U. D. *17*, 187*
Reh, Emma *14*, 193
Rembolt, R. R. *8*, 115
Rhoades, C. P. *16*, 13*
Rhoads, Paul S. *4*, 178*
Richey, F. D. *16*, 54
Riegl, M. *8*, 177
Riggs, T. R. *9*, 47
Ringrose, R. C. *3*, 33
Riquelme, Natividad Segovia *16*, 195
Roberts, Lydia J. *13*, 48*
Rojas, Marta *15*, 62

Salcedo, Juan, Jr. *3*, 84*
Salmon, W. D. *12*, 87*
Samuels, Leo T. *11*, 126*
Sarkar, Nirmal *15*, 110
Sarrett, H. F. *9*, 47
Sauberlich, H. E. *12*, 87*
Scarano, E. *6*, 141
Schendel, H. E. *12*, 198-A
Schneider, Burch H. *16*, 154*; *16*, 189*; *17*, 103
Schneider, Morton *6*, 55
Schou, Mogens *15*, 179*
Schultz, F. W. *1*, 5*
Schultze, M. O. *16*, 143*
Schweet, Richard S. *12*, 180*
Scott, D. B. McNair *1*, 30
Scoular, Florence I. *11*, 208*
Scrimshaw, Nevin S. *4*, 200*; *14*, 193*
Scrufutis, Helen C. *13*, 9
Sealock, R. R. *6*, 90*
Seibert, Helen *8*, 35
Shaw, M. S. *3*, 156*
Sheets, Olive *3*, 173*
Sheiness, Phyllis *10*, 60
Shemin, David *6*, 201*
Sherman, Henry C. *4*, 107*; *7*, 139; *13*, 16*
Shive, William *6*, 212*
Shukers, Carroll F. *17*, 70
Shull, Kenneth H. *14*, 223
Shuster, L. *6*, 147

Siberman, D. J. *15*, 62
Silberberg, Martin *4*, 210*
Silberberg, Ruth *4*, 210*
Sims, Edith S. *17*, 70
Sinclair, H. M. *16*, 196*
Singer, Thomas P. *6*, 132*
Slanetz, C. A. *9*, 102*
Smith, Louise F. *3*, 136*
Snell, Esmond E. *1*, 20; *9*, 72*
Snodgrass, R. M. *15*, 62
Sobel, Albert E. *16*, 105*
Sobotka, Harry *8*, 204*
Spies, Tom D. *15*, 1*; *15*, 62*
Sprinson, David B. *12*, 213*
Squibb, R. L. *4*, 200
Sreenivasan, A. *12*, 161*; *15*, ST*; *16*, S*
Stare, Fredrick, J. *3*, 51*; *7*, 52*; *11*, 98*
Stein, M. H. *8*, 12; *8*, 38
Steinkamp, Ruth *17*, 70
Stekol, Jakob A. *12*, 106*
Stern, Joseph R. *6*, 151; *6*, 211*
Stewart, B. *8*, 177
Still, Jack *15*, 110
Stone, R. E. *15*, 62
Storvick, Clara A. *1*, 113*
Stotz, E. *1*, 11
Stout, Anne K. *1*, 20
Strength, D. R. *17*, 171
Strong, F. M. *1*, 20; *2*, 25*
Stumpf, P. K. *6*, 50
Subrahmanyan, V. *16*, 202*
Sure, Barnett *12*, 128*; *17*, 36*
Suzuki, Shichi *7*, 209

Talman, Ellen *11*, 100
Tatum, E. L. *12*, 68*; *16*, 40
Taylor, Henry L. *11*, 175*
Taylor, R. M. *10*, 91
Templeton, Frances *3*, 85
Tenbrinck, Margaret *8*, 35
Tenmatay, Augusto *1*, 206-A*
Theophilus, F. *15*, 176
Thompson, R. C. *1*, 20
Todd, W. R. *11*, 100*
Tompkins, Winslow T. *8*, 76*
Totter, John R. *17*, 70*
Touster, Oscar *16*, 150*
Touverud, Kirsten *8*, 115
Trubey, Robert H. *6*, 212
Tung, Ta Cheng *3*, 163*

Uzman, L. *8*, 97

Vallee, Bert L. *1*, 188*
Van Eck Willem F. *7*, 181*
Van Itallie, T. B. *14*, 223
Van Landingham, Floy B. *1*, 26

Van Slyke, Donald D. *16*, 14*
Van Wagtendonk, W. J. *9*, 18
Vignos, P. J. *6*, 141
Vilter, Carl F. *15*, 62
Vinvi, V. J. *8*, 42
Visser, Donald W. *9*, 119*
Viswanathan, K. S. *8*, 167*

Waelsch, Heinrich *10*, 45*; *10*, 60*
Wald, George *10*, 23*; *11*, 129*
Waldman, Jerome *16*, 65
Wang, T. P. *6*, 147
Wasserman, Elga *2*, 77
Waterlow, John *15*, ST*
Weaver, David S. *3*, 155*
Weech, A. E. *12*, 7*
Weissman, N. *1*, 11
Weisz-Tabori, E. *6*, 55
Wells, Ruth I. *3*, 85
Westerman, Beulah, D. *3*, 85*
Weswig, P. H. *6*, 80
White, Virginia *1*, 30
Wilbur, Karl M. *7*, 118
Wilkins, Walter *5*, 71*
Williams, J. N. Jr. *12*, 162*
Williams, R. J. *1*, 20*
Williams, Virginia R. *7*, 209*
Williams, W. T. *1*, 86
Wilson, D. Wright *6*, 144
Winn, James *8*, 35
Winters, Jet C. *3*, 66*; *4*, 19*
Wolbach, S. Burt *8*, 97*
Wolf, George *12*, 182*
Woll, Ephraim *8*, 168*
Wollenberger, Albert *10*, 23
Woodside, Gilbert L. *16*, 124*
Woodyard, Ella *10*, 59
Wooster, R. C. *9*, 47
Wortis, H. *8*, 12; *8*, 38
Wright, A. M. *8*, 42; *12*, 43
Wright, H. V. *17*, 174
Wright, L. D. *1*, 20
Wu, Pei Hzing Lin *12*, 182
Wulzen, Rosalind *9*, 18*
Wylie, Ruth C. *10*, 6

Yang C. S. *8*, 177
Yanofsky, C. *2*, 77
Yenermen, Munevver *15*, ST*
Yost, Don M. *1*, 3*
Yudkin, W. H. *11*, 129

Zarudnaya, K. *6*, 50
Zatman, L. J. *6*, 147
Zelitch, I. *6*, 151
Zmachinsky, W. C. *13*, 16
Zuckerman, Richard *1*, 138

NOTE: This list does not contain the names of all co-workers on Williams-Waterman Fund grants since principal investigators have not reported these to us uniformly. It is, however, complete as far as our records are concerned.

COLLEGE LIBRARY
ST.
JOSEPH